Elementary Mathematical Programming

NEW YORK · JOHN WILEY & SONS, INC.

London · Chapman & Hall, Ltd.

Elementary Mathematical Programming

ROBERT W. METZGER

Industrial Engineering Department

General Motors Institute

Library of Congress Catalog Card Number: 58-13466

Printed in the United States of America

Preface

This textbook is an attempt to fill a need for an elementary description of several of the methods of mathematical programming. Most of the material written to date concerning mathematical programming has been in one of two general categories. The first category contains numerous articles written by management consultants, who are primarily concerned with presenting mathematical programming in very nontechnical terms as a useful tool for management. Hence these articles present the subject in terms much too general to permit any useful study. The second category contains several textbooks and numerous articles written by operations research people for fellow operations research analysts. This category presents the highly technical side of mathematical programming and is totally beyond the comprehension of all but mathematicians.

This book is designed to bridge the gap between these two categories. None of the mathematics is sacrificed except perhaps in the terminology used. Each of the methods is presented in a logical sequence and illustrated by typical yet simple problems. Some may feel that the text belabors some points; however, it is written for those with a minimum mathematical background, although it is to be hoped that the more mathematically mature reader will not be unduly bored by the detail.

This book is designed primarily for people in business and industry. It is designed so both the manager, who desires a cursory knowledge, and the industrial engineer or management analyst, who wants to know how to solve problems with these methods, can obtain the information they desire. This book is also suitable as a text in a one-semester introductory course in mathematical programming and as a supplementary text in an introductory course in operations research. The various methods are presented via sample problems in a logical step-by-step pattern. The examples throughout the book are carefully chosen to aid the reader's understanding. One thing is developed at a time so the reader is exposed, in sequence, to various facets of the problems and of the solution methods. Every solution technique is summarized in a detailed listing of the step-by-step method.

The methods and their various refinements and extensions are presented, but the proofs of the various theorems are omitted. One does not require the elaborate mathematical proof of a method in order to use it effectively. Liberal footnoting and the extensive bibliography provide suitable references for the student interested in further study in this and allied areas of operations research. It is hoped that this book may be an adequate primer, in the methods of mathematical programming and the general philosophy of operations research, for further study in these fields.

Chapter 1 provides some general introductory and background material about operations research and mathematical programming. Chapters 2, 3, and 4 present the three groups of methods, namely distribution, simplex, and approximation methods, respectively. Here the sample problems are purposely simple so as not to confuse the reader. In fact, most of the sample problems used to illustrate the various methods can be rather easily solved by inspection.

Chapter 5 contains the complete solution and analysis of two typical industrial problems; a manufacturing and a blending problem. This chapter stresses the development of a suitable formulation and the interpretation of the final solution(s). Chapter 6 discusses the applicability of high-speed computers for solving problems and mentions several of the available computer programs which will accomplish the solution of mathematical programming problems. Chapters 7, 8, 9, and 10 illustrate the details of various problems solved via mathematical programming. These problems, though they are hypothetical, are none the less based upon real industrial problems. In each of these problems, as in Chapter 5, the formulation and postsolution analysis are stressed.

Many thanks are due my supervisor, L. C. Lander Jr., who helped to generate my initial interests in this area of study. Mr. Lander has always been most cooperative and understanding during the several years of study culminating in this textbook. Many of my colleagues have been most helpful in their several comments and criticisms. Several of them, particularly H. C. Charbonneau, G. E. Johnson, W. S. Klappich, and G. L. Webster, served as very competent students in faculty training sessions to allow me to develop the text and general classroom lecture format. To these men I owe a major debt of gratitude.

The several students who were members of the initial class in mathematical programming at General Motors Institute during the fall term 1956 and the class of the spring term 1957 were most helpful in the final phase of polishing and "debugging" the lecture outlines. The students of this initial group were the ones who gave greatest impetus to the development of this material.

Many thanks are due Mrs. B. C. Mize for the initial typing and proofreading, and last, but far from least, to my wife without whose assistance and encouragement this book would not have been a physical reality.

ROBERT W. METZGER

Flint, Michigan
October 1958

Contents

1. Introduction

Mathematical programming is one of the many facets of the field of operations research. In order to appreciate the full potentialities of mathematical programming, it may be well to look briefly at operations research and what it is. Operations research, as such, actually was born shortly before World War II when civilian scientists were called in by the British Armed Forces to assist in solving problems in the radar warning network protecting the British Isles. This effort grew enormously during the war years and spread to all branches of the allied forces. The primary effort was directed toward analysis and solution of various tactical problems in all branches of the allied armed forces. Operations research actually contributed immeasurably to the allied victory.

Actually operations research was not new in the history of war. In fact, numerous generals have occasionally called upon various scholars and mathematicians for the solution to various tactical problems during the many centuries of armed conflict. Indeed much of the work of F. W. Lanchester in England and Thomas A. Edison in the United States during and after World War I was similar to World War II operations research. Lanchester attempted to analyze mathematically the relationships among victory, numerical superiority, and firepower and published his work, undertaken primarily as a hobby, in 1916.[1] Thomas A. Edison, while a member of the Naval Consulting Board, conducted numerous studies of antisubmarine warfare.[2] The work of both these men was, however, considered of academic interest only and had no effect upon operations during World War I. The widespread success of operations research during World War II was due, in part to organizational relationships. The Naval Consulting Board of World War I was a group of civilian advisers who reported to a civilian, the Secretary of the Navy, whereas the operations research personnel of World War II were attached to and reported directly to military command personnel. Operations research teams, having met with success in military problems, turned to British and American industry during the postwar period to apply their military proven techniques to solving industrial problems. In many instances the results arrived at by these operations research teams were little more than those that would have been achieved by the application of good common sense. This, in general, caused management to dismiss operations research summarily as just a new name for the same thing industry has been doing by committee for years. This attitude on the part of management plus the often highly sophisticated and complicated notation and writing of operations researchers has been the principal cause of the relatively slow acceptance of the techniques of operations research within industry.

Operations research differs from almost anything else industry has done in the past, chiefly in method and approach to a problem. The techniques of operations research require an exacting statement of the problem with all the variables and factors included with their proper interrelationships. This requirement causes a formulation of the problem which before this time was usually overlooked. Once this habit of precise formulation of problems is established, then the new viewpoint of operations research is possible in attacking industrial problems.

Mathematical programming can best be defined as the techniques used to find the optimum relationship between a number of inter-

---

[1] F. W. Lanchester, *Aircraft in Warfare: The Dawn of the Fourth Arm,* Constable & Co., London, 1916.

[2] W. F. Whitmore, "Edison and Operations Research," *Journal of the Operations Research Society of America,* V. 1, No. 2, February 1953, pp. 83–85. See also Lloyd N. Scott, *Naval Consulting Board of the United States,* Government Printing Office, Washington, 1920.

dependent variables—or a means of obtaining the very best course of action where many courses of action exist. This is the bare essence of mathematical programming, and to some it may appear over simplified. However, this definition will be extended and modified as the text progresses.

Mathematical programming has been successfully applied in the following areas:

1. **Product allocation**—with a number of jobs that can run on a number of different machines, it is possible to determine how to best allocate the work to the machines so as to minimize either the total time or total cost to produce the entire work load.

2. **Distribution and shipping**—with a product demand at various locations and a supply of product at several warehouses, it is possible to determine which warehouse should ship how much product to which customer so that the total distribution costs are a minimum.

3. **Market research** (specifically locating factories, warehouses, and outlets)—it is possible to determine the best of several possible warehouse, or factory or outlet locations from various facts about each location.

4. **Job and salary evaluation**—here mathematical programming is used in place of multiple correlation analysis to determine the relative weights of the factors considered. This applies to salary and executive-type jobs. A similar analysis can be applied to any testing situation to give a better over-all evaluation.

5. **Blending**—applied to blending oils, gasolines, alloy elements, etc. It is possible to determine either how to blend available ingredients or what ingredients to obtain to meet at minimum cost a specific end-product demand.

6. **Materials handling**—one of the newer areas of application. This presents an approach that can increase hand or nonautomated material handling utilization upwards to 80 per cent. A typical problem is expanded later in the text.

7. **Production planning**—it is possible to develop the lowest-cost producing plan, starting with a sales forecast, available plant capacity, and the tangible cost factors. A typical production planning problem is expanded later in the text.

Mathematical programming consists of many various techniques and methods. This book will not attempt to cover them all, but will include the most widely used methods. They are:

1. Distribution methods.
    a. Stepping-stone method.

  b. Modified-distribution method.
  c. Vogel's approximation method.
2. Simplex method.
3. Approximation methods.

The distribution methods can be applied to situations of product distribution to several customers from several sources of supply so that the distribution costs are a minimum. Consider the problem faced by a planning clerk who has factories at Janesville, St. Louis, and Flint, and must plan shipment of products to customers at various locations throughout the United States. The problem is then to determine how to supply the customer demand such that the over-all transportation cost is a minimum. The modified-distribution method and Vogel's approximation method make larger problems of this type better suited to hand computation.

Problems of distribution do not lend themselves readily to obtaining the best solution by trial-and-error methods. A leading food processor is saving thousands of dollars annually in shipping costs through an application of the distribution method.

The simplex method is more generally applicable to solving other types of industrial problems. Although the simplex method involves matrix algebra, one does not have to be a mathematician to use this method effectively. In fact, a knowledge of high school algebra is sufficient for most applications of the simplex method. This does not, however, preclude the fact that the services of a mathematician are often desirable and occasionally necessary.

Approximation methods can be and are employed in some cases, several of which will be discussed later. These approximation methods do not yield the absolutely best solution, but they do permit a good solution to be obtained rapidly and economically. This is very useful where the precise answer may not be worth the added work or may require more time than is available. Use of the precise mathematical formulation rather than an approximation may require the use of computing equipment when either the formulation is very large or complex or the answer is required in an absolute minimum of time on a repetitive basis. Some of the approximation methods are not general but are tailor-made for a particular situation. They are, however, based upon the mathematical formulation.

The distribution methods will be considered first. Since these are the easiest to learn and understand, they will serve as a good introduction to the methodology of mathematical programming. The methods are presented via illustrative problems. Several specific applications of the distribution methods to solving industrial problems are also presented.

The more general simplex method is presented, and a few sample problems are developed. One section is devoted to several of the approximation methods. A sample problem is used to illustrate two of the approximation methods.

Applications are included to present an over-all picture of the types of problems to which these techniques apply, and to assist in associating the problem statement, the formulation, and the interpretation and use of the final results.

2. Distribution Methods

One of the earliest published accounts of a scientific method for formulating and solving distribution or transportation problems appeared[3] in 1941. World War II subsequently saw considerable development of the techniques of linear programming and operations research. In 1951 considerable advance was given to linear programming by the Cowles Commission,[4] and particularly to the solution of distribution problems by G. B. Dantzig[5] and T. C. Koopmans.[6] At this stage, however, the methods were still difficult for a nonmathematician to understand.

The first really simplified approach, the "stepping-stone" method was presented in 1953 by W. W. Cooper and A. Charnes.[7] The

---

[3] "The Distribution of a Product from Several Sources to Numerous Localities," Frank L. Hitchcock, *Journal of Mathematics & Physics,* V. 20, 1941, pp. 224–230.

[4] T. C. Koopmans, ed., *Activity Analysis of Production and Allocation,* Cowles Commission monograph 13; John Wiley & Sons, 1951.

[5] *Ibid.,* Part 4, Chapter XXIII.

[6] *Ibid.,* Part 2, Chapter XIV.

[7] W. W. Cooper and A. Charnes, "Transportation Scheduling by Linear Programming," *Proceedings of the Conference on Operations Research in Marketing,* Case Institute, January, 1953. See also A. Charnes and W. W. Cooper, "The Stepping

"stepping-stone" approach was improved somewhat[8] in 1954 and further refined to become the modified-distribution method[9] which appeared in 1955.

Work since 1955 by individuals such as H. W. Kuhn,[10] M. M. Flood, P. S. Dwyer[11] has contributed to and advanced other techniques for solving problems of distribution. These methods, however, are somewhat beyond this text and hence will not be covered here. Dr. B. A. Galler has done some work in solving multidimensional distribution problems,[12] and has developed a very suitable approximate method which is superior, in terms of solution time and cost, to the more general simplex method.

This chapter will explain the "stepping-stone" method and then give a complete description of the modified-distribution method, via a simple yet typical problem. The last portion of the chapter presents Vogel's approximation method as a useful technique for more efficient hand solution of distribution problems. The approximation method of Dr. Galler is discussed but not in too much detail here since the calculations are better suited to machine computation. However, this method is again discussed in a subsequent chapter on machine computation in mathematical programming.

A DISTRIBUTION PROBLEM

Consider an organization with warehouses in three locations: Flint, Janesville, and St. Louis. An order dispatcher must determine how to distribute a product most economically from these

---

Stone Method of Explaining Linear Programming Calculations in Transportation Problems," *Management Science,* V. 1, No. 1, October 1954.

[8] A. Henderson and R. Schlaifer, "Mathematical Programming: Better Information for Better Decision Making," *Harvard Business Review,* May–June 1954, pp. 73–100.

[9] R. O. Ferguson, "Linear Programming," *American Machinist,* Special Report No. 389, McGraw-Hill Publishing Co., 1955.

[10] H. W. Kuhn, "The Hungarian Method for the Assignment Problem," *Naval Research Logistics Quarterly,* V. 2, 1955, pp. 83–97.

[11] P. S. Dwyer, *The Solution of the Hitchcock Transportation Problem with a Method of Reduced Matrices,* University of Michigan (hectographed), December 1955.

See also "Maximum Group Assembly Sums," a report prepared for the director, Detachment 4 (Crew Research Laboratory) Air Force Personnel and Research Center, Randolph Air Force Base, Randolph Field, Texas.

[12] B. A. Galler, "704 Program for the Approximate Solution of the Multi-dimensional Transportation Problem," General Motors Research Staff Report No. 34–782 (privately circulated), November 1956.

three warehouses to four customers. The warehouses have the following quantities of this product in stock:

Warehouse Location	
Flint	150 units
Janesville	40 units
St. Louis	80 units
Total Supply	270 units

The four customers have the following demand:

Customer Location	
Chicago	90 units
Cleveland	70 units
Dayton	50 units
Minneapolis	60 units
Total Demand	270 units

It costs \$0.10 per unit per mile to transport this product. The problem is then—what warehouse should ship how much product to what customers so that the total distribution costs are minimum?

The first step is to determine the distribution costs per unit from each of the three warehouses to each of the four customers. The mileage between warehouses and customers can be obtained from a map or suitable route tables and is as follows:

From \ To	Chicago	Cleveland	Dayton	Minneapolis
Flint	270	230	310	690
Janesville	100	450	400	320
St. Louis	300	540	350	570

Mileage Chart

Since it costs \$0.10 per unit per mile to distribute this product then the distribution costs per unit will be as follows:

From \ To	Chicago	Cleveland	Dayton	Minneapolis
Flint	\$27.00	\$23.00	\$31.00	\$69.00
Janesville	10.00	45.00	40.00	32.00
St. Louis	30.00	54.00	35.00	57.00

Shipping Costs per Unit

If we eliminate the statement that the distribution of the product should be at a minimum cost, then many solutions to this problem may be obtained. A more or less standard approach to a problem like this is to assign the shipments on the basis of lowest cost insofar as possible. Many such approaches to this problem can be made, but usually the orders will be assigned as they are received by the dispatching clerk. Assuming that the orders are received first from Dayton, then Cleveland, and Chicago, and Minneapolis, then the dispatcher could assign them as follows:

The demand for 50 units at Dayton can be satisfied by Flint at the lowest cost. Flint will also supply the 70 units required by the customer in Cleveland. The customer in Chicago will receive 40 units from Janesville (this is the entire supply at Janesville) and 30 units from Flint. This exhausts the supply at Flint. The remaining 20 units required by the Chicago customer must be shipped from St. Louis. Finally the customer at Minneapolis will receive his 60 units from St. Louis.

The assignments are then as follows:

From	To	Units
Flint	Dayton	50
Flint	Cleveland	70
Janesville	Chicago	40
Flint	Chicago	30
St. Louis	Chicago	20
St. Louis	Minneapolis	60

Notice that the supply exactly equals the demand. Although this is usually not the case in a real situation, it was chosen here because it simplifies the problem formulation. In a later section the situation of unequal supply and demand will be considered.

The above solution to the problem meets all the customer demand without overtaxing the warehouse supplies. Though this is a possible solution to the problem, is it the most economical?

By reorganizing the problem it might be easier to analyze. Figure 1 is similar to the cost table but has the added advantage of presenting all of the relevant data in a concise manner.

The figures in the small boxes are taken from the cost table, and the circled figures represent the shipping assignments previously made. The supply and demand figures appear at the right and along the bottom of the table. Hence, in one table we have the entire problem and a solution.

With such an organization of the problem, it may be possible to realize a better shipping plan by spending some time inspecting the table.

From \ To	Chicago	Cleveland	Dayton	Minneapolis	Supply
Flint	27 (30)	23 (70)	31 (50)	69	150
Janesville	10 (40)	45	40	32	40
St. Louis	30 (20)	54	35	57 (60)	80
Demand	90	70	50	60	270 / 270

Fig. 1. Distribution Table—Initial Solution

For example, every unit shipped to Minneapolis from Janesville rather than from St. Louis will realize a savings of $25.00. However, for every unit shipped by Janesville to Minneapolis, a unit must be shipped from St. Louis to Chicago at an increase in cost of $20.00. Such a change would then net a reduction in distribution costs of $5.00 per unit. Since 40 units can be changed in this fashion, the total reduction in distribution costs will be $200.00, which certainly makes the time spent in inspection worth while.

The improved solution would then be as given in Figure 2.

The costs of the two solutions can be quickly compared by calculating the total distribution costs (Tables 1 and 2).

From \ To	Chicago	Cleveland	Dayton	Minneapolis	Supply
Flint	27 (30)	23 (70)	31 (50)	69	150
Janesville	10	45	40	32 (40)	40
St. Louis	30 (60)	54	35	57 (20)	80
Demand	90	70	50	60	270 / 270

Fig. 2. Distribution Table—an Inspection Solution

Table 1. Initial Solution

From	To	No. of Units	Cost per Unit	Total Cost
Flint	Chicago	30	$27.00	$ 810.00
Flint	Cleveland	70	23.00	1610.00
Flint	Dayton	50	31.00	1550.00
Janesville	Chicago	40	10.00	400.00
St. Louis	Chicago	20	30.00	600.00
St. Louis	Minneapolis	60	57.00	3420.00
		270 units		$8390.00 Total distribution cost

Table 2. Inspection Solution

From	To	No. of Units	Cost per Unit	Total Cost
Flint	Chicago	30	$27.00	$ 810.00
Flint	Cleveland	70	23.00	1610.00
Flint	Dayton	50	31.00	1550.00
Janesville	Chicago	40	32.00	1280.00
St. Louis	Chicago	20	30.00	1800.00
St. Louis	Minneapolis	60	57.00	1140.00
		270 units		$8190.00 Total distribution cost

The inspection solution shows a savings of $200.00 over the initial solution. However, is this solution the very best? Further inspection, much like that used to improve the initial solution, might yield further improvement in the shipping program if such is possible.

Simple distribution problems may be reasonably easy to solve by relatively informal inspection techniques. However, this type of approach is totally useless in more complicated problems. Hence, the real need is for an organized and more systematic procedure to optimize distribution problems. Optimize is a term used to mean minimization of costs or maximization of profits whichever the case may be in a problem.

"STEPPING-STONE" METHOD

The "stepping-stone" method is one of the systematic methods for optimizing distribution problems. The basis and proof for this method will not be discussed here. However, we will be able to see how it does optimize via the previous problem. The stepping-stone method permits any size distribution problem to be systematically solved with the very best solution resulting.

The stepping-stone method and all other systematic methods use the previously presented distribution tables except that the form is now called a distribution matrix. Mathematically a matrix is an array of numbers—so is a distribution table. Hence it can be called a distribution matrix.

In mathematical programming, costs are always assigned a negative (−) sign, and profits are always assigned a positive (+) sign. This retains the same mathematics whether working with costs or profits, and will permit the same mathematics to be applied to maximizing profits and minimizing costs in distribution problems.

The stepping-stone method is really little more than an inspection method itself, and has been replaced, for the most part, by the modified-distribution method. However the stepping-stone method is the basis for and serves as a good introduction to the modified-distribution method.

The distribution matrix for the problem discussed previously is shown in Figure 3. Note that the costs are now shown as negative numbers.

The distribution matrix is a 3×4 array (i.e.; three warehouses and four customers). Matrices are generally dimensioned as $m \times n$, where m is the number of rows and n is the number of columns.

The northwest-corner initial solution will be used to begin the problem. The northwest-corner solution is one of arbitrary assignments beginning at the upper left corner of the matrix and assigning consecutively to the right and down until all assignments have been made. The northwest-corner initial solution for this problem is shown in Figure 4.

From \ To	Chicago	Cleveland	Dayton	Minneapolis	Supply
Flint	−27	−23	−31	−69	150
Janesville	−10	−45	−40	−32	40
St. Louis	−30	−54	−35	−57	80
Demand	90	70	50	60	270 \ 270

Fig. 3. Distribution Matrix

To / From	Chicago	Cleveland	Dayton	Minneapolis	Supply
Flint	−27 (90)	−23 (60)	−31	−69	150
Janesville	−10	−45 (10)	−40 (30)	−32	40
St. Louis	−30	−54	−35 (20)	−57 (60)	80
Demand	90	70	50	60	270 / 270

Fig. 4. Northwest-Corner Initial Solution

In actual practice almost any initial solution could be used. However, for the present, the northwest-corner initial solution will be used.

Several parts of Figure 4 can be named for easy reference. The supply and demand figures are commonly referred to as rim conditions. The circled numbers (assignments) are called *stones.* The squares containing a circled number (an assignment) will be called *stone squares.* The squares with no circled numbers will be called *water squares.* Basically then the problem is to move about the stones (circled assignments) until the distribution costs are minimum. Hence the name "stepping stone" applies rather well. If each square in the matrix is identified by its row and column location, then it will be easier to refer to the matrix. For example, square 24 would be the square in the second row and fourth column.

In order to determine how and where to move the stones or assignments, the improvement possibility of the water squares must be investigated. Consider the improvement possibility of water square 13 (first row, third column). The improvement possibility can be most easily determined by examining the resulting changes in costs if one unit was assigned to that water square (in this case examining the costs if one unit was shipped from Flint to Dayton). Of course, if one unit was shipped from Flint to Dayton, it would be necessary to modify some of the other assignments in the shipping plan so as not to deviate from the rim conditions of the problem.

In this particular situation, if a unit is shipped from Flint to Dayton (square 13), then one unit must be deducted from the shipment from Flint to Cleveland (square 12). Similarly, if one less unit is sent from Flint to Cleveland, then one more unit must be sent from Janesville to Cleveland. Finally, if one unit more is sent from Janesville to Cleveland, then one unit less can be sent to Dayton. This last item is satisfactory since Dayton is receiving one more unit from Flint. These changes in the shipping program can be much more readily seen in Figure 5.

From \ To	Chicago	Cleveland	Dayton	Minneapolis	Supply
Flint	−27 (90)	− −23 (60)	+ −31	−69	150
Janesville	−10	+ −45 (10)	− −40 (30)	−32	40
St. Louis	−30	−54	−35 (20)	−57 (60)	80
Demand	90	70	50	60	270 / 270

Fig. 5. Required Changes in Shipping Assignments to Evaluate the Improvement Possibility of Shipping from Flint to Dayton in Preference to the Initial Shipping Assignments

The changes in the initial shipping assignments are noted in the matrix array by the plus and minus signs in the upper left-hand corner of squares 13, 12, 22, and 23. Note how these plus and minus signs indicate the required changes in the preceding paragraph. Note also that a plus *and* a minus sign appear in each of two rows and two columns. This permits changes in the shipping program which will still abide by the requirements of the respective rim conditions.

Actually the changes in the shipping program can be more easily explained. In order to evaluate the improvement possibility of a selected water square, one must establish a closed path (moving horizontally and vertically only) from this water square via stone squares back to the same water square. A right-angle turn is made only at stone squares in the path, though the path may skip over stone and water squares. (This latter point does not occur at this time in the problem. However, it will be illustrated soon.) Alternate plus and minus signs are established along this path beginning with a plus sign in the selected water square. The path and the alternate plus and minus signs may be established either clockwise or counterclockwise; it makes no difference. Actually one could say that a closed path is established stepping only on stones at every turn in the path beginning at a selected water square. Hence the name "stepping-stone" method. In the particular problem at hand, the closed path could not include square 11 because one would soon have wet feet stepping in a water square in the first column. Actually, if the initial solution has been properly established, one and *only one* closed path is possible for any water square.

The improvement possibility or evaluation of water square 13 can be easily determined by examining the cost changes. The plus and minus signs along the closed path indicate where a unit will be added or subtracted and hence where a shipping cost will be accrued (+) or saved (−). Tabulating the costs will show the per unit gain or loss of this change in the shipping program.

Costs Accrued	Costs Saved
\$31 (square 13)	\$23 (square 12)
45 (square 22)	40 (square 23)
\$76.00	\$63.00

Note: If the problem was expressed as profit, then the comparison would be profit gained versus profit lost.

This change would then result in a net increase in shipping costs of \$13.00 per unit. Obviously this is no improvement, and so square 13 can be temporarily set aside as offering no advantage at this stage of the problem. The investigation can then proceed to another water square.

A similar analysis is conducted for every water square until one is found that shows improvement. Hence it is usually advisable to proceed in some orderly fashion, evaluating the water squares column by column or row by row (so as not to miss any) until a water square indicates possible improvement. It is usually a good idea also to erase the plus and minus signs in the closed path when a selected water square shows no improvement possibility.

Another closed path of alternate plus and minus signs must be established in order to evaluate the improvement possibility of square 14. Figure 6 illustrates this closed path.

It can be seen in Figure 6 that the closed path skips over two water squares, and affects several more shipments. In the analysis

From \ To	Chicago	Cleveland	Dayton	Minneapolis	Supply
Flint	−27 (90)	− −23 (60)	−31	+ −69	150
Janesville	−10	+ −45 (10)	− −40 (30)	−32	40
St. Louis	−30	−54	+ −35 (20)	− −57 (60)	80
Demand	90	70	50	60	270 / 270

Fig. 6. Required Shipping Changes in Evaluating the Improvement Possibility of Square 14, Flint to Minneapolis

for water square 13, three assignments in the shipping program were affected. In the analysis for water square 14, all but one of the shipping assignments in this problem are affected. This is due to the high degree of interrelationship between shipments, which is characteristic of problems of this kind, and is the major reason why most solution methods by inspection usually fail, particularly in more complex problems.

The evaluation of water square 14 is:

Costs Accrued	Costs Saved
\$ 69 (square 14)	\$ 23 (square 12)
45 (square 22)	40 (square 23)
35 (square 33)	57 (square 34)
\$149.00	\$120.00

Obviously then water square 14 offers no improvement at this time since the above change would accrue \$29.00 more cost per unit. The analysis can then proceed to water square 21.

The required changes in the shipping program to evaluate water square 21 are as shown in Figure 7.

The evaluation is:

Costs Accrued	Costs Saved
\$10 (square 21)	\$27 (square 11)
23 (square 12)	45 (square 22)
\$33.00	\$72.00

To / From	Chicago	Cleveland	Dayton	Minneapolis	Supply
Flint	− −27 (90)	+ −23 (60)	−31	−69	150
Janesville	+ −10	− −45 (10)	−40 (30)	−32	40
St. Louis	−30	−54	−35 (20)	−57 (60)	80
Demand	90	70	50	60	270 / 270

Fig. 7. Required Shipping Changes in Evaluating the Improvement Possibility of Square 21, Janesville to Chicago

Water square 21 offers an improvement possibility of saving \$39.00 per unit shipped from Janesville to Chicago in preference to the initial shipping program. Rationally then one should attempt to ship as much as possible to attain the maximum possible gain. The number of units that can be changed is dictated by the smallest stone at a negative place in the closed path—ten units in this case. If any more than ten units are changed, the assignment in square 22 would become negative, implying that Cleveland would supply Janesville. Since this is unrealistic in the real problem, the stones (assignments) must be handled so they are all positive or zero.

The shipping program is then improved by adding or subtracting the ten units as indicated by the signs in the closed path (illustrated in Figure 8).

The shipping program is thus improved. The reduction in the shipping costs with this improved solution should be \$390.00, since ten units were changed and the water-square evaluation indicated a \$39.00 per unit reduction in cost. This can be easily verified by comparing the total costs of the initial and improved solution (Tables 3 and 4).

This solution is best called the first improved solution since further improvement may yet be possible.

The water squares in the first improved solution must then be evaluated in the same manner as described previously. Every water square, including the ones evaluated in the initial northwest corner solution, must be evaluated until one is found that yields an

From \ To	Chicago	Cleveland	Dayton	Minneapolis	Supply
Flint	−(80) −27 ~~(90)~~	+(70) −23 ~~(60)~~	−31	−69	150
Janesville	+ −10 (10)	− −45 ~~(10)~~	−40 (30)	−32	40
St. Louis	−30	−54	−35 (20)	−57 (60)	80
Demand	90	70	50	60	270 / 270

Fig. 8. Changes in Initial Shipping Program

improvement possibility. The entire procedure is successively repeated until finally all the water squares show no further improvement. The optimum shipping program is obtained when no further improvement is possible in any water square.

Table 3. Initial Northwest-Corner Solution

Square	No. of Units	Cost per Unit		Total Cost
11	90	$27.00		$2430.00
12	60	23.00		1380.00
22	10	45.00		450.00
23	30	40.00		1200.00
33	20	35.00		700.00
34	60	57.00		3420.00
			Total	$9580.00

Table 4. First Improved Solution

Square	No. of Units	Cost per Unit		Total Cost
11	80	$27.00		$2160.00
12	70	23.00		1610.00
21	10	10.00		100.00
23	30	40.00		1200.00
33	20	35.00		700.00
34	60	57.00		3420.00
			Total	$9190.00

To / From	Chicago	Cleveland	Dayton	Minneapolis	Supply
Flint	−27 (80)	−23 (70)	−31	−69	150
Janesville	−10 (10)	−45	−40 (30)	−32	40
St. Louis	−30	−54	−35 (20)	−57 (60)	80
Demand	90	70	50	60	270 / 270

Fig. 9. First Improved Shipping Program

The basic parts of the stepping-stone method can be summarized into a step-by-step procedure as follows:

1. Express the problem in a distribution matrix array.
2. Establish an initial solution. (Note: Use the Northwest-corner initial solution for the time being. Later on, any initial solution can be used.)
3. Evaluate the water squares one by one in an orderly fashion (either row by row or column by column) until one is found that shows an improvement possibility.
   a. Establish a closed path (moving horizontally and vertically only) from the selected water square via stone squares back to the same water square. A right-angle turn is made only at stone squares, though the path may skip over stone and water squares. There will be one and only one such closed path for each water square in any particular shipping assignment.
   b. Establish alternate plus and minus signs on this path, starting with a plus in the selected water square. (Note: The closed path and the alternate plus and minus signs may be established either clockwise or counter-clockwise. It makes no difference.)
   c. Determine the improvement possibility by comparing the costs accrued (indicated by + places in the closed path) and the costs saved (indicated by − places in the closed path).
   d. If no improvement exists, then repeat step 3 with another water square.

4. When a water square is found that shows an improvement possibility then add or subtract (as indicated by the signs on the closed path) the amount of the smallest stone at a negative place in the path.
5. Repeat steps 3 and 4 until no further improvement is possible. The solution is then optimum.

The stepping-stone method then is a rather simple iterative[13] method. However, one can see how this method can become rather tedious in larger more complex problems. The modified-distribution method, while it is based upon and uses much the same terminology as the stepping-stone method, is a considerably more efficient method for solving distribution problems.

THE MODIFIED-DISTRIBUTION METHOD

The modified-distribution method (this will be abbreviated MODI method from here on) is very similar to the stepping-stone method except that it offers a more efficient means of determining the water-square evaluations. The MODI method can be most easily described via the preceding distribution problem.

Here, as with the stepping-stone method, the initial solution will be the rather arbitrary northwest-corner solution. Later on more freedom is allowed in establishing an initial solution.

From \ To	Chicago	Cleveland	Dayton	Minneapolis	Supply
Flint	−27 (90)	−23 (60)	−31	−69	150
Janesville	−10	−45 (10)	−40 (30)	−32	40
St. Louis	−30	−54	−35 (20)	−57 (60)	80
Demand	90	70	50	60	270 / 270

Fig. 10. Initial Northwest-Corner Solution

[13] To iterate means to repeat. Hence a method where the same procedures are used over and over again is an iterative one.

The MODI method deviates from the stepping-stone method in that, once an initial solution is established, then a number is calculated for each row and column. This number depends upon the particular solution and the cost factors of the problem and is used to evaluate the water squares. If we let R and K stand for the row and column values and attach a subscript to denote the specific row and column, then

$$R_i = \text{numerical value assigned to row } i$$

and

$$K_j = \text{numerical value assigned to column } j$$

If we also let

C_{ij} = cost in square ij (the square at the junction of row i and column j)

then it is possible to establish the R_i and K_j values by the formula:

$$R_i + K_j = \text{cost (or profit) at } \textit{stone square } ij$$

In the problem at hand, the relationships for determining the R and K values are:

1. $R_1 + K_1 = C_{11}$ (cost at stone square 11)

and, since there is a stone in square 12,

2. $R_1 + K_2 = C_{12}$

and, similarly,

3. $R_2 + K_2 = C_{22}$
4. $R_2 + K_3 = C_{23}$
5. $R_3 + K_3 = C_{33}$
6. $R_3 + K_4 = C_{34}$

This exhausts the occurrences of stone squares. Note that the square number, the subscripts on the costs, and the R and K subscripts check. This assures that the cost being considered is the one at the junction of the specific row and column. This type of notation (subscripts i for row and j for column) is rather common in matrix work. The statement $R_1 + K_4 = C_{14}$ is *not* true, since square 14 is a water square and not a stone square.

The various costs (C_{ij}'s) can be read from the distribution matrix. Hence the above equations present seven variables combined in only six equations. In order to establish the R and K

values, it is necessary to assume a value for an R or a K. This is completely legitimate since the significance of the R and K values is not their absolute numerical value but rather their interrelated values. It will be shown later how any value for any R or K will not affect the subsequent analysis. Here the R_1 value will be assumed as zero. This will be done throughout the succeeding discussion. If

$$R_1 = 0$$

then, from (1),

$$K_1 = C_{11} - R_1 = -27 - 0$$
$$K_1 = -27$$

Likewise, from (2),

$$K_2 = C_{12} - R_1 = -23 - 0$$
$$K_2 = -23$$

and similarly so the R and K values are

$$R_1 = 0, \qquad K_1 = -27$$
$$R_2 = -22, \qquad K_2 = -23$$
$$R_3 = -17, \qquad K_3 = -18$$
$$K_4 = -40$$

It does not hold true that the R and K values will always be negative. They may be positive, negative, or zero, depending on the problem. The distribution matrix with the R and K values included is shown in Figure 11.

From \ To	$K_1 = -27$	$K_2 = -23$	$K_3 = -18$	$K_4 = -40$	Supply
$R_1 = 0$	−27 (90)	−23 (60)	−31	−69	150
$R_2 = -22$	−10	−45 (10)	−40 (30)	−32	40
$R_3 = -17$	−30	−54	−35 (20)	−57 (60)	80
Demand	90	70	50	60	270 / 270

Fig. 11. Initial Solution—*R* and *K* Values Established

Practice at computing R and K values will show that this can usually be done mentally instead of writing out the equations as above. With all the R's and K's computed, the next step is to evaluate each water square. This is accomplished in the following manner:

$$R + K - (\text{cost}) = \text{water-square evaluation}$$

If the result is positive (+), then no improvement possibility exists in that water square. If the result is negative (−), then further improvement is possible.

Each water square can then be evaluated as shown in Table 5.

Table 5

Water Square	Equation	Improvement
13	$R_1 + K_3 - C_{13} =$	
	$0 + (-18) - (-31) = +13$	No
14	$R_1 + K_4 - C_{14} =$	
	$0 + (-40) - (-69) = +29$	No
21	$R_2 + K_1 - C_{21} =$	
	$(-22) + (-27) - (-10) = -39$	Yes
24	$R_2 + K_4 - C_{24} =$	
	$-22 + (-40) - (-32) = -30$	Yes
31	$R_3 + K_1 - C_{31} =$	
	$-17 + (-27) - (-30) = -14$	Yes
32	$R_3 + K_2 - C_{32} =$	
	$-17 + (-23) - (-54) = +14$	No

This indicates that three water squares show improvement possibility. Any of these three could be selected to improve the solution. However, if the water square with the most negative evaluation is selected, then the best solution will generally be obtained most rapidly.

The water-square evaluation here is exactly the same as that obtained with the stepping-stone method. In the stepping-stone method, the evaluation for water square 13 was:

Costs Accrued	Costs Saved
−31 (square 13)	−23 (square 12)
−45 (square 22)	−40 (square 23)
−76	−63

If in this analysis we always subtract the costs accrued from the costs saved (or profits gained from profits lost), the same water-square evaluation (same value and same sign) will always result.

Water square 21 has the greatest negative evaluation and will therefore be used to improve the solution. The closed path with alternate plus and minus signs is then established, and the solution is improved in the same manner as in the stepping-stone method. The closed path and the changes in the initial assignments are illustrated in Figure 12. Note that the initial assignments have been crossed out and the new assignments made. Note also that the rim conditions (supply and demand) are still met. This change in the solution essentially involved adding and subtracting the same quantity from each of two rows and two columns, thereby leaving the rim conditions unchanged.

From \ To	$K_1 = -27$	$K_2 = -23$	$K_3 = -18$	$K_4 = -40$	Supply
$R_1 = 0$	− (80) −27 ~~(90)~~	+ (70) −23 ~~(60)~~	−31	−69	150
$R_2 = -22$	+ −10 (10)	− −45 ~~(10)~~	−40 (30)	−32	40
$R_3 = -17$	−30	−54	−35 (20)	−57 (60)	80
Demand	90	70	50	60	270 / 270

Fig. 12. Changes in Initial Assignments

Thus far the MODI method has accomplished the same improvement as was obtained with the basic stepping-stone method. The first improved solution (Figure 13) will have a total cost of \$390.00 less than the initial solution. The amount of improvement will always be equal to the water-square evaluation times the number of units moved.

Changing the solution makes some if not all of the *R* and *K* values incorrect. New values for *R* and *K* must be established in order to determine if further improvement is possible. The formulas for the *R* and *K* values may be written out, or the *R* and *K* values may be calculated mentally and placed on the distribution matrix.

From \ To	$K_1 =$	$K_2 =$	$K_3 =$	$K_4 =$	Supply
$R_1 = 0$	−27 (80)	−23 (70)	−31	−69	150
$R_2 =$	−10 (10)	−45	−40 (30)	−32	40
$R_3 =$	−30	−54	−35 (20)	−57 (60)	80
Demand	90	70	50	60	270 / 270

Fig. 13. First Improved Solution

From \ To	$K_1 = -27$	$K_2 = -23$	$K_3 = -57$	$K_4 = -79$	Supply
$R_1 = 0$	−27 (80)	−23 (70)	−31	−69	150
$R_2 = +17$	−10 (10)	−45	−40 (30)	−32	40
$R_3 = +22$	−30	−54	−35 (20)	−57 (60)	80
Demand	90	70	50	60	270 / 270

Fig. 14. First Improved Solution with *R* and *K* Values

Figure 14 shows the first improved solution and the proper R and K values. Note that the R and K values are not all negative as with the initial solution.

The water-square evaluations can now be made, using the relationship $R + K -$ cost at a water square (Table 6).

Since water square 24 shows the greatest improvement possibility, this will be used to improve the solution. With practice, the water-square evaluations can be accomplished mentally, thereby greatly speeding the solution process.

Next, it is necessary to establish the closed path beginning with the selected water square 24 and moving via stone squares back to square 24. Alternate plus (+) and minus (−) signs are assigned along this path as illustrated in Figure 15.

Table 6

Water Square	Relationship	Improvement
13	$R_1 + K_3 - C_{13} =$ $0 + (-57) - (-31) = -26$	Yes
14	$R_1 + K_4 - C_{14} =$ $0 + (-79) - (-69) = -10$	Yes
22	$R_2 + K_2 - C_{22} =$ $17 + (-23) - (-45) = +39$	No
24	$R_2 + K_4 - C_{24} =$ $17 + (-79) - (-32) = -30$	Yes
31	$R_3 + K_1 - C_{31} =$ $22 + (-27) - (-30) = +25$	No
32	$R_3 + K_2 - C_{32} =$ $22 + (-23) - (-54) = +53$	No

From \ To	$K_1 = -27$	$K_2 = -23$	$K_3 = -57$	$K_4 = -79$	Supply
$R_1 = 0$	−27 (80)	−23 (70)	−31	−69	150
$R_2 = +17$	−10 (10)	−45	− −40 (30)	+ −32	40
$R_3 = +22$	−30	−54	+ −35 (20)	− −57 (60)	80
Demand	90	70	50	60	270 / 270

Fig. 15. Solution Improvement

Again the amount to be moved must be determined; in this case 30 units from square 23. The amount to be moved is the smallest stone at a negative place along the closed path.

Placing this amount (30 units) in square 24 and adding and subtracting this amount from the stones along the path will yield the second improved solution. These changes are illustrated in Figure 16.

To / From	$K_1 =$	$K_2 =$	$K_3 =$	$K_4 =$	Supply
$R_1 = 0$	−27 (80)	−23 (70)	−31	−69	150
$R_2 =$	−10 (10)	−45	−40	−32 (30)	40
$R_3 =$	−30	−54	−35 (50)	−57 (30)	80
Demand	90	70	50	60	270 / 270

Fig. 16. Second Improved Solution

Here, as before, the savings, reduction in distribution costs, can be easily verified by calculating and comparing the costs for the first and second improved solutions. The reduction in cost here is $900.00.

Again the entire procedure is repeated. Mathematically this is called iteration, this step beginning the third iteration.

The *R* and *K* values are established, and the water-square evaluations are computed. Then the closed path is selected as shown in Figure 17. Note that the water-square evaluations have been marked just below the cost box in each water square. Since the solution method is concerned with only negative water-square evaluations, these are the only ones noted. The rest are merely denoted by the plus (+) sign.

Water square 31 has the greatest negative evaluation. The closed path is illustrated, and the alternate plus and minus signs are established along this path. The amount to be moved is the smallest stone at a negative place on the closed path—in this case 10 units.

The revisions can now be made and the third improved solution (Figure 18) will result.

Again the same process is followed in establishing *R* and *K* values and then evaluating the water squares. This is presented

From \ To	$K_1 = -27$	$K_2 = -23$	$K_3 = -27$	$K_4 = -49$	Supply
$R_1 = 0$	−27; (80)	−23; (70)	−31; +	−69; +	150
$R_2 = +17$	− −10; (10)	−45; +	−40; +	+ −32; (30)	40
$R_3 = -8$	+ −30; −5	−54; +	−35; (50)	− −57; (30)	80
Demand	90	70	50	60	270 / 270

Fig. 17. Second Improved Solution with Third Improvement Shown

From \ To	$K_1 =$	$K_2 =$	$K_3 =$	$K_4 =$	Supply
$R_1 = 0$	−27; (80)	−23; (70)	−31	−69	150
$R_2 =$	−10	−45	−40	−32; (40)	40
$R_3 =$	−30; (10)	−54	−35; (50)	−57; (20)	80
Demand	90	70	50	60	270 / 270

Fig. 18. Third Improved Solution

in Figure 19. Since the water-square evaluation of square 13 is the only negative one, then it is used to further improve the solution. The closed path is also shown.

The changes are then made by moving 50 units so that the fourth improved solution appears as in Figure 20.

The same process of establishing R and K values and evaluating the water squares is repeated again. However, this time all the water-square evaluations are positive, indicating that no further improvement is possible in the solution. Consequently, the fourth

To / From	$K_1 = -27$	$K_2 = -23$	$K_3 = -32$	$K_4 = -54$	Supply
$R_1 = 0$	− −27 (80)	−23 (70)	+ −31 −1	−69 +	150
$R_2 = +22$	−10 +	−45 +	−40 +	−32 (40)	40
$R_3 = -3$	+ −30 (10)	−54 +	− −35 (50)	−57 (20)	80
Demand	90	70	50	60	270 / 270

Fig. 19. Third Improved Solution with Fourth Improvement Shown

To / From	$K_1 =$	$K_2 =$	$K_3 =$	$K_4 =$	Supply
$R_1 = 0$	−27 (30)	−23 (70)	−31 (50)	−69	150
$R_2 =$	−10	−45	−40	−32 (40)	40
$R_3 =$	−30 (60)	−54	−35	−57 (20)	80
Demand	90	70	50	60	270 / 270

Fig. 20. Fourth Improved Solution

improved solution is really the optimum (lowest distribution cost) solution.

Summary—The Basic MODI Method. The optimum solution to the problem presented here could be obtained readily by inspection. However, the modified-distribution (MODI) method is a method that can be employed to solve distribution problems of any size and degree of complexity.

It is to be noted that every change made at the various stages of the MODI solution to the problem was rectangular—the closed path had just four corners and never crossed itself. This does not have to be so. If, in the first improvement of the solution, water square 31 were selected, then the closed path would be as shown in Figure 21.

To / From	$K_1 =$	$K_2 =$	$K_3 =$	$K_4 =$	Supply
$R_1 = 0$	− −27 (90)	+ −23 (60)	−31	−69	150
$R_2 =$	−10	− −45 (10)	+ −40 (30)	−32	40
$R_3 =$	+ −30	−54	− −35 (20)	−57 (60)	80
Demand	90	70	50	60	270 / 270

Fig. 21. A Closed Path for Square 31

The problem discussed here involved costs. If a problem with profit figures had been used, exactly the same mathematics would apply. Since profit will be shown as positive numbers, the mathematics will maximize the total profit. Some practice at several problems should serve to clarify this. Actually the techniques of mathematical programming are algebraically maximizing methods. Mathematically speaking, to maximize a negative quantity algebraically is to minimize the absolute value of that quantity.

A definite significance can be attached to the water-square evaluations. As previously pointed out, the water-square evaluation can be used to predict the savings for each step toward the solution. The water-square evaluations in the final solution may be useful in developing alternative solutions, either equally optimum or less-than-optimum solutions. This will be explained later.

The basic MODI method can then be summarized in the following steps:

1. Establish the problem matrix.
2. Determine (temporarily at least) the northwest-corner initial solution.
3. Establish R and K values.

$$R_1 = 0$$
$$R + K = \text{cost (profit) at a stone square}$$

4. Evaluate the water squares.

$$R + K - \text{cost (profit) at a water square}$$

If the result is (+), then no improvement is possible.
If the result is (−), then further improvement is possible.

5. Select the water square with the most negative evaluation.

6. Establish the closed path (moving horizontally and vertically only) from this water square via stone squares and back to the same water square. A right-angle turn is made only at stones in the path. The path may skip over stone and water squares. There will be one and only one such closed path.

7. Place alternate plus (+) and minus (−) signs on the path starting with a plus (+) at the selected water square.

8. Select the amount to be placed in the selected water square as the smallest stone at a negative place on the closed path.

9. Place that smallest stone in the selected water square.

10. Add or subtract (according to the sign along the closed path) the amount of the smallest stone (step 8) from every stone along the closed path.

11. Repeat steps 3 through 10 as often as necessary until no negative water square evaluations exist. At that time the optimum answer is obtained.

VARIATIONS AND RESTRICTIONS

The problem discussed in the preceding section had supply equal to demand. In actual practice, this is seldom if ever so. Several situations such as unequal supply and demand and other restrictions will be illustrated and discussed here.

Unequal Supply and Demand. The situation where supply exceeds or is less than demand is often encountered in distribution problems. Consider the same problem as the one discussed previously except with the supply at Flint reduced to 140 units. This is shown in Figure 22.

The initial northwest-corner solution would then be as shown in Figure 23.

It can be seen from the initial northwest-corner solution that the customer at Minneapolis is arbitrarily short 10 units on his order. Application of the MODI method then will always result in the customer at Minneapolis being short 10 units. It would be better if the mathematics of the problem were allowed to determine who is to be short on his (their) order(s). This can be accomplished by adding another row to the matrix as shown in Figure 24.

To / From	Chicago	Cleveland	Dayton	Minneapolis	Supply
Flint	−27	−23	−31	−69	140
Janesville	−10	−45	−40	−32	40
St. Louis	−30	−54	−35	−57	80
Demand	90	70	50	60	260 / 270

Fig. 22. Distribution Matrix—Unequal Supply and Demand

To / From	Chicago	Cleveland	Dayton	Minneapolis	Supply
Flint	−27 (90)	−23 (50)	−31	−69	140
Janesville	−10	−45 (20)	−40 (20)	−32	40
St. Louis	−30	−54	−35 (30)	−57 (50)	80
Demand	90	70	50	60	260 / 270

Fig. 23. Unequal Supply and Demand—Initial Northwest-Corner Solution

This new row is designated as a dummy warehouse supplying 10 nonexistent units. The zero costs are assigned, since the units do not exist and hence will never be distributed. This dummy warehouse can now distribute the 10 nonexistent units to any customer(s), which in essence means that any customer may be short-changed on his order. The addition of the dummy warehouse and its supply also balances the rim conditions (supply and demand) of the problem. The rim conditions must be balanced before the solution method can be applied successfully.

The dummy row is handled as any other row in the problem matrix. The initial problem was 3×4 (3 rows by 4 columns) and

From \ To	Chicago	Cleveland	Dayton	Minneapolis	Supply
Flint	−27 (90)	−23 (50)	−31	−69	140
Janesville	−10	−45 (20)	−40 (20)	−32	40
St. Louis	−30	−54	−35 (30)	−57 (50)	80
Dummy	0	0	0	0 (10)	10
Demand	90	70	50	60	270 / 270

Fig. 24. Initial Solution—Rim Conditions Balanced

is now 4 × 4. The MODI method can now be employed to determine the lowest-cost solution which will also determine how the shortage in supply will be allocated to the customers.

In this particular problem it so happens that the customer at Minneapolis is short 10 units on his order. The optimum solution for this problem is shown in Figure 25.

From \ To	Chicago	Cleveland	Dayton	Minneapolis	Supply
Flint	−27 (20)	−23 (70)	−31 (50)	−69	140
Janesville	−10	−45	−40	−32 (40)	40
St. Louis	−30 (70)	−54	−35	−57 (10)	80
Dummy	0	0	0	0 (10)	10
Demand	90	70	50	60	270 / 270

Fig. 25. Optimum Solution

Much the same procedure would be followed if supply were greater than demand. In such a situation, a dummy customer (dummy column) with suitable product demand will be created. The unutilized or undistributed supply is used to satisfy this dummy customer demand. This type of problem can easily be expanded to include the inventory costs at the various warehouses if they differ significantly.

Other Restrictions. The distribution methods permit many other restrictions to be considered. For example: Assume in the preceding problem of unequal supply and demand that management says that the customer at Minneapolis cannot be short on his order. This factor can be included in the problem by merely assuming a prohibitively large distribution cost from the dummy warehouse to the Minneapolis customer. The cost used is $-M$. The factor $-M$ is defined as so large that it dominates all else in the problem.

Two approaches are possible when solving such a problem. They are:

1. Include all the restrictions in the initial formulation of the problem. The solution obtained will be the one required.

2. Formulate and solve the somewhat less restricted problem; then assess the solution in terms of the additional restrictions.

The second approach can provide slightly more information about the solution. If, for example, the above problem had been stated initially with the added restriction that both Chicago and Minneapolis must receive their entire orders, then the first approach would require a $-M$ cost to be established in the dummy row for the first and fourth columns. The solution would then be the one that management requires. If, however, the second approach were used, the dummy would be set up with all zero cost elements, and the economics of the problem would dictate who is to be short on his order. This would be a somewhat less restricted formulation. If either Chicago or Minneapolis were shortchanged in the optimum solution for this formulation, then the $-M$ cost factor could be inserted and a proper optimum solution obtained. However, this second approach, while it yields the same solution, also provides additional information from the less restricted solution. It is possible to show any increase in distribution costs due to the additional restrictions. This information can serve as a guide to better management decisions on this and perhaps future problems.

There are many points both pro and con for the two approaches.

Actually the objective of the problem and the preference of the individual will determine which approach is taken. Either approach will yield the optimum solution but not necessarily the same total evaluation of the problem.

In general, whenever a possible course of action is arbitrarily canceled, the $-M$ cost factor can be employed in the distribution matrix. This is further illustrated in the following problem.

Consider a distribution problem in which a factory supplies three distributorships who in turn supply the customers with the product. The data are as follows:

Factory supply	250 units
Distributorship capacity:	
Flint	150 units
Janesville	40 units
St. Louis	80 units
	270 units *capacity*
Customer requirements	
Chicago	90 units
Cleveland	70 units
Dayton	50 units
Minneapolis	50 units
	260 units *required*

Distribution costs from the various distributorships to the customers are the same as in the previously discussed problem. The problem is then to determine how to distribute the factory supply to the customers via the distributorships so that the total distribution costs are a minimum.

Inspection of the preceding information will reveal two conditions that must be included in the problem formulation. These are:

1. Ten units of customer demand must be left unsatisfied because the factory supply is only 250 units.

2. Twenty units of distribution capacity will be unutilized, again because the factory supply is only 250 units.

Each of these situations can be included in the problem matrix. A dummy distributor with a supply of 10 units will accomplish the first condition. A dummy customer with a demand of 20 units will accomplish the second condition. These are illustrated in Figure 26.

Note the costs that have been assigned to the dummy distributor

From \ To	Chicago	Cleveland	Dayton	Minneapolis	Dummy	Capacity
Flint	−27	−23	−31	−69	0	150
Janesville	−10	−45	−40	−32	0	40
St. Louis	−30	−54	−35	−57	0	80
Dummy	0	0	0	0	−M	10
Demand	90	70	50	50	20	280 / 280

Fig. 26. Distribution Matrix—Restricted Factory Supply

and customer. The $-M$ cost has been assigned for C_{45} (fourth row, fifth column) for two reasons. These are:

1. The dummy distributor must distribute its supply of nonexistent units to the real physical customers.

2. The dummy customer must be satisfied by the real physical distributors.

This formulation will accomplish the restrictions of the problem. Note how the $-M$ cost factor is used to cancel out a possible course of action. This problem is interesting from another standpoint. Initially one might be prone to think that the totals for the rim conditions cannot exceed 270 units, when in reality the rim conditions can total to almost any quantity so long as they balance. The optimum solution to the problem shown in Figure 26 is as follows:

Customer	No. of Units	From
Chicago	30	Flint
	60	St. Louis
Cleveland	70	Flint
Dayton	50	Flint
Minneapolis	40	Janesville
Total	250	

The customer at Minneapolis is short-changed 10 units, and the distributor at St. Louis has 20 units of capacity unutilized. This problem does exhibit the fact that some logic and reasoning are required in balancing the rim conditions. One cannot merely add a dummy row or column with a suitable quantity to make the rim conditions balance. If only one dummy were used in the above problem, it would be possible to balance the rim conditions. However the distribution matrix would not be a valid representation of the problem. Often it pays to note the conditions or results that must be obtained in a problem (i.e.; customers short 10 units; distributors 20 units below capacity) prior to establishing the distribution matrix.

Degeneracy. When a distribution problem is said to be degenerate, the problem may cycle (go around in circles) and never attain an optimum or the problem may collapse before an optimum solution is obtained. Obviously this can be caused by errors in the work. However, it may be caused by the nature of the particular problem. In distribution problems, degeneracy can be caused by similar rim conditions and is evidenced by an insufficient number of stones. Consider one of the previous problems with slightly modified rim conditions as shown in Figure 27.

From \ To	Chicago	Cleveland	Dayton	Minneapolis	Supply
Flint	−27	−23	−31	−69	150
Janesville	−10	−45	−40	−32	40
St. Louis	−30	−54	−35	−57	80
Demand	90	60	60	60	270 / 270

Fig. 27. A Degenerate Problem

The northwest-corner initial solution would then be as shown in Figure 28.

The degeneracy will be evident in attempting to establish R and K values. If $R_1 = 0$, then K_1 and K_2 can be determined. Here it is impossible to proceed further. Note that the stair-step pattern

From \ To	Chicago	Cleveland	Dayton	Minneapolis	Supply
Flint	−27 ⑨⓪ (90)	−23 (60)	−31	−69	150
Janesville	−10	−45	−40 (40)	−32	40
St. Louis	−30	−54	−35 (20)	−57 (60)	80
Demand	90	60	60	60	270 \ 270

Fig. 28. Degenetate Problem—Initial Northwest-Corner Solution

of the usual northwest-corner solution is missing. Actually the problem matrix can be partitioned into two disconnected parts. The degeneracy can be resolved by inserting a zero stone (⓪) wherever needed. Here it can be inserted in square 22 as shown in Figure 29.

The remaining R and K values can now be determined. The zero stone is handled the same as any other stone in the matrix. The zero stone means nothing as far as the real physical problem is concerned. It is merely a computational gimmick which permits the same solution method to still be applied and solve the problem.

Actually there is considerable latitude concerning the placement

From \ To	$K_1 = -27$ Chicago	$K_2 = -23$ Cleveland	$K_3 =$ Dayton	$K_4 =$ Minneapolis	Supply
$R_1 = 0$ Flint	−27 (90)	−23 (60)	−31	−69	150
$R_2 =$ Janesville	−10	−45 (0)	−40 (40)	−32	40
$R_3 =$ St. Louis	−30	−54	−35 (20)	−57 (60)	80
Demand	90	60	60	60	270 \ 270

Fig. 29. Degeneracy Resolved

of a zero stone in an initial solution. However, only the correct number of stones must be used. It can be seen from the previous examples that $m + n - 1$ (where m = number of rows and n = number of columns in a matrix) represents the correct number of stones or assignments. If less than $m + n - 1$ stones exist, as in Figure 28, then the problem is degenerate.[14] This statement applies similarly to any step in the solution method. When more than $m + n - 1$ stones exist, then an error has been made.

The maximum possible degeneracy occurs in distribution problems where the supply at each of the various warehouses is one unit and the demand for each customer is one unit. In problems with such unity rim conditions, many successive improvements via the MODI method may mean changing only the position of zero stones, resulting in no reduction in the total cost. However repeated application of the MODI method will still obtain the best solution. Distribution problems with unity rim conditions are more generally known as assignment problems. Several special techniques have been developed for solving assignment problems. However, they will not be covered here since the MODI method provides a suitable means for solving these problems.

Degeneracy can occur in an initial solution as in the previous example or at any step during the solution method or in the optimum solution. Consider the problem in Figure 30 to illustrate degeneracy encountered during the solution.

From \ To	$K_1 = -3$	$K_2 = -4$	$K_3 = -3$	Supply
$R_1 = 0$	−3 (2)	−4 (8)	−5 +	10
$R_2 = -3$	−8 +	−7 (2)	−6 (7)	9
$R_3 = -3$	−2 −4	−4 −3	−6 (2)	2
Demand	2	10	9	21

Fig. 30. A Degenerate Problem

[14] See G. B. Dantzig, "Application of the Simplex Method to a Transportation Problem" in Koopman's *Activity Analysis of Production and Allocation,* p. 360.

Square 31 (third row, first column) has the greatest negative water-square evaluation. If it is selected to improve the solution, then the closed path is as shown in Figure 31.

The improved solution would then be as shown in Figure 32.

To / From	$K_1 = -3$	$K_2 = -4$	$K_3 = -3$	Supply
$R_1 = 0$	− (2) [−3]	+ (8) [−4]	[−5]	10
$R_2 = -3$	[−8]	− (2) [−7]	+ (7) [−6]	9
$R_3 = -3$	+ [−2]	[−4]	− (2) [−6]	2
Demand	2	10	9	21

Fig. 31. Changes in Initial Solution

To / From	$K_1 =$	$K_2 =$	$K_3 =$	Supply
$R_1 = 0$	[−3]	(10) [−4]	[−5]	10
$R_2 =$	[−8]	[−7]	(9) [−6]	9
$R_3 =$	(2) [−2]	[−4]	[−6]	2
Demand	2	10	9	21

Fig. 32. Degenerate Improved Solution

It can be seen from Figure 31 that the problem is now degenerate. There were five stones previously whereas there are only three now. To circumvent this degeneracy, two of the stones at a negative place in the closed path (Figure 31) should have been left as zero stones. This would present the improved solution as shown in Figure 33.

To / From	$K_1 = +1$	$K_2 = -4$	$K_3 = -3$	Supply
$R_1 = 0$	−3	−4 (10)	−5	10
$R_2 = -3$	−8	−7 (0)	−6 (9)	9
$R_3 = -3$	−2 (2)	−4	−6 (0)	2
Demand	2	10	9	21

Fig. 33. Improved Solution—Degeneracy Resolved

Obviously several choices exist for selecting the position of the zero stone(s). An incorrect choice is indicated if in the next step of the MODI method the most negative water square is found to be one of the squares where the zero stone could have been placed. (In the problem shown in Figure 33, this would occur if water square 11 had the greatest negative evaluation.) If the MODI method is followed, the next step will undo what was done in the preceding step, or the problem will begin to cycle. This can be avoided by merely moving the zero stone and continuing with the MODI method.

Another technique involves the insertion of a small quantity usually designated as ε (epsilon). The ε is added and subtracted from two rows and two columns when there are insufficient assignments. The epsilon is handled as any other regular assignment. In succeeding steps, the epsilon is removed as soon as a sufficient number of real assignments exist. This approach is considerably more difficult than using zero stones—particularly in hand computation. However, the ε must be used in machine computation because an electronic computor cannot distinguish between a zero where there is no assignment and an assignment of zero with a circle around it.

Alternative Solutions. The water-square evaluations are used to improve the solution step by step, and can be used to determine the economics of alternative solutions. The water-square evaluations in the final (optimum) matrix indicate the per unit increase in cost or decrease in profit for all the possible alternative courses of action. If, in the final matrix one or more water-square evaluations are zero, then there are several equally optimum alternative solutions (several solutions with identical total cost or profit). Often the information about the cost or profit differential for the alternative courses of action is as valuable to management as the optimum solution.

Summary. The modified distribution (or MODI) method offers a relatively simple method of solving distribution-type problems. Subsequent chapters will expand the applications of this method to solving industrial problems.

The MODI method is best summarized in the following steps:

1. Set up the problem distribution matrix.

2. Balance the rim conditions (supply and demand).

3. Establish an initial solution:

  a. Northwest-corner solution.

  b. Inspection solution.

  Note: The number of stones or assignments $= m + n - 1$.

4. Establish R and K values:

$$R_1 = 0$$

$$R + K = \text{cost or profit at an intersecting stone square}$$

  a. Resolve degeneracy as may be necessary with zero stones (⓪).

5. Evaluate each water square.

$$R + K - (\text{cost or profit of the water square})$$

  a. If the above is positive (+), then no further improvement exists in that water square at this step in the solution.

  b. If the above is negative (−), then further improvement is possible.

6. Select the water square with the greatest negative evaluation from step 5.

  a. Establish a closed path (moving horizontally or vertically only) from this selected water square via stone squares back to the same water square. A right-angle turn is made only at stones in the path. This path can skip over stone and water squares as may be necessary. There will be one and only one such closed path for a water square.

  b. Establish alternate plus (+) and minus (−) signs on this path, starting with a plus (+) in the selected water square. This will permit balanced rim conditions to exist.

7. Determine the amount to be placed in the selected water square. This will be the smallest stone at a negative place in the closed path.

8. Make the necessary changes by adding or subtracting the selected amount from every stone in the path as indicated by the alternate plus and minus signs.
9. Re-establish *R* and *K* values as may be necessary.
10. Repeat steps 5 through 10 until all water-square evaluations are plus or zero.

The interpretation of the water-square evaluations is as follows:

1. A positive number indicates the per unit increase in cost (or decrease in profit) that would result when a stone or assignment of one unit is placed in the water square and the necessary adjustments are made in the remainder of the program.

2. A negative number indicates the per unit decrease in cost (or increase in profit) that would result when a stone or assignment of one unit is placed in the water square and the necessary adjustments are made in the remainder of the program.

3. When one or more water-square evaluations are zero and the remaining evaluations are all positive, then there exists one or more equally optimum alternative solutions to the problem.

4. Mathematically speaking, if two equally optimum solutions exist, then an infinite number of equally optimum alternative solutions exist for the problem. However, this is not true where the assignments are integers (whole numbers). Then a finite number of solutions will exist.

The MODI method discussed here is completely general and applies equally well, regardless of the order of the various rows and columns. The discussion here dealt mainly with costs and profits. Actually any measure can be used. However, it must be recognized that all the mathematical programming methods are algebraically maximizing techniques. Hence, when something is to be maximized, it is expressed in positive numbers, and, if it is to be minimized, it must be expressed in negative numbers. Actually to maximize a negative number algebraically is to minimize the absolute value of that number.

VOGEL'S APPROXIMATION METHOD

In the preceding discussion it was noted that the work involved in solving distribution-type problems can be materially reduced if a better initial solution is obtained. Vogel's approximation method is a method whereby a very good initial solution to distribution-type problems can always be obtained. In fact, Vogel's approximation method will yield the optimum solution initially in the majority of distribution problems. This method together with the MODI method can take much of the tedium out of solving distribution problems.

Vogel's approximation method (which henceforth will be abbreviated VAM) was developed in late 1955 as the result of informal research by W. R. Vogel.[15] The method was, to a large extent, intuitively developed, and, though it has no formal mathematical proof, it has proved its value and validity in solving many distribution-type problems.

The VAM will be presented via the same problem used to illustrate the basic MODI method. The distribution matrix for the problem is shown in Figure 34.

From \ To	Chicago	Cleveland	Dayton	Minneapolis	Supply
Flint	−27	−23	−31	−69	150
Janesville	−10	−45	−40	−32	40
St. Louis	−30	−54	−35	−57	80
Demand	90	70	50	60	270 / 270

Fig. 34. Distribution Matrix

The VAM can best be presented in a series of steps which will be applied to the problem represented in Figure 34.

1. Determine the differences (absolute differences) between the two most (algebraically) maximum elements (cost or profit values) for each row and each column of the matrix.

[15] W. R. Vogel, Chief, Training Branch, Ordnance Management Engineering Training Program, Rock Island Arsenal, and also associated with N. V. Reinfeld in the National Institute of Management, management consultants with headquarters in Cleveland, Ohio.

The calculation for the first column would be as follows:

Most maximum element	−10
Second most maximum element	−27
Difference	17

The difference may be noted at the top or bottom of the first column. We prefer to note the difference above the column outside the boundaries of the matrix so as not to confuse the VAM numbers and subsequent *K* values. The sign of the difference is of no consequence since the VAM uses the absolute values of the differences calculated.

The calculation for the second column would be as follows:

Most maximum element	−23
Second most maximum element	−45
Difference	22

This too can be noted at the top of the second column. The calculations are continued for every column and row. The calculation for the first row would be as follows:

Most maximum element	−23
Second most maximum element	−27
Difference	4

This may be noted at either end of the row. We prefer here to note the differences for the rows to the right of the row and outside the boundaries of the matrix so that these differences will not be confused with the values in the rim conditions or with subsequent *R* values. All the row and column differences are noted in Figure 35.

2. Select the row or column with the greatest difference.

In the problem at hand the fourth column would be so selected.

3. Assign as much as possible to the square with the most (algebraically) maximum element in that selected row or column.

In this case, square 24 (second row, fourth column) has the most algebraically maximum element (−32), and hence 40 units would be assigned there as shown in Figure 36.

It can be seen that to assign any less than 40 units would violate the statement of step three, and to assign any more than 40 units would exceed the supply at Janesville, thereby violating the rim conditions of the problem.

	17	22	4	25		
From \ To	Chicago	Cleveland	Dayton	Minneapolis	Supply	
Flint	−27	−23	−31	−69	150	4
Janesville	−10	−45	−40	−32	40	22
St. Louis	−30	−54	−35	−57	80	5
Demand	90	70	50	60	270 / 270	

Fig. 35. Distribution Matrix—VAM Differences Noted

	17	22	4	25		
From \ To	Chicago	Cleveland	Dayton	Minneapolis	Supply	
Flint	−27	−23	−31	−69	150	4
Janesville	−10	−45	−40	−32 (40)	40	22
St. Louis	−30	−54	−35	−57	80	5
Demand	90	70	50	60	270 / 270	

Fig. 36. Distribution Matrix—One Assignment Made by the VAM

4. Cross out the row or column completely utilized or satisfied by the assignment.

In this problem the second row would be crossed out since it has been completely utilized by this assignment. In crossing out a row or column, care should be taken to do this rather lightly since the crosses will be erased later.

5. Redetermine the differences as may be necessary, but omit the row(s) and column(s) crossed out.

In the problem at hand this would mean to redetermine the differences, omitting the second row of the matrix. The difference for the first column would be calculated as follows:

Most maximum element	−27
Second most maximum element	−30
Difference	3

Obviously this is the only possible difference for the first column since only two squares exist for consideration.

The remaining differences can be calculated and noted as before.

	3 ~~17~~	31 ~~22~~	4	12 ~~25~~		
From \ To	Chicago	Cleveland	Dayton	Minneapolis	Supply	
Flint	−27	−23	−31	−69	150	4
Janesville	−10 ✕	−45 ✕	−40 ✕	−32 (40)	40	~~22~~
St. Louis	−30	−54	−35	−57	80	5
Demand	90	70	50	60	270 / 270	

Fig. 37. Distribution Matrix—Step 5 of VAM Accomplished

It can be seen in Figure 37 that the old row and column differences are crossed out where they no longer apply. The difference for the second row (22) has been crossed out also since the second row is no longer available for consideration.

6. Repeat steps 2 through 5 until all assignments are made.

Reapplying step 2 would cause the second column to be selected. The assignment would be 70 units in the first row, and the problem would appear now as shown in Figure 38.

This second assignment will completely fill the demand represented by the second column; hence that column is crossed out.

Reapplying the VAM will yield the succeeding assignments as illustrated in Figures 39 and 40.

	3 ~~17~~	31 ~~22~~	4	12 ~~25~~		
From \ To	Chicago	Cleveland	Dayton	Minneapolis	Supply	
Flint	−27	−23 (70)	−31	−69	150	4
Janesville	−10 X	−45 X	−40 X	−32 (40)	40	~~22~~
St. Louis	−30	−54 X	−35	−57	80	5
Demand	90	70	50	60	270 / 270	

Fig. 38. Distribution Matrix—Second Assignment Accomplished with VAM

	3 ~~17~~	~~31~~ ~~22~~	4	12 ~~25~~		
From \ To	Chicago	Cleveland	Dayton	Minneapolis	Supply	
Flint	−27	−23 (70)	−31	−69 X	150	4
Janesville	−10 X	−45 X	−40 X	−32 (40)	40	~~22~~
St. Louis	−30	−54 X	−35	−57 (20)	80	5
Demand	90	70	50	60	270 / 270	

Fig. 39. Distribution Matrix—Third Assignment with VAM

After the fourth assignment has been made, it can be seen that the VAM can no longer be applied. However, only two squares (11 and 13) remain open, and these will permit the remaining assignments to be made merely by inspection. The complete assignments are shown in Figure 41.

This completes the application of VAM. However, it does not necessarily complete the problem.

	3 ~~17~~	~~31~~ ~~22~~	4	~~12~~ ~~25~~		
From \ To	Chicago	Cleveland	Dayton	Minneapolis	Supply	
Flint	−27	(70) −23	−31	× −69	150	4
Janesville	× −10	× −45	× −40	(40) −32	40	~~22~~
St. Louis	(60) −30	× −54	× −35	(20) −57	80	5
Demand	90	70	50	60	270 / 270	

Fig. 40. Distribution Matrix—Fourth Assignment with VAM

	3 ~~17~~	~~31~~ ~~22~~	4	~~12~~ ~~25~~		
From \ To	Chicago	Cleveland	Dayton	Minneapolis	Supply	
Flint	(30) −27	(70) −23	(50) −31	−69	150	4
Janesville	−10	−45	−40	(40) −32	40	~~22~~
St. Louis	(60) −30	−54	−35	(20) −57	80	5
Demand	90	70	50	60	270 / 270	

Fig. 41. VAM Initial Solution

7. When all assignments have been made, then apply the MODI method to improve the solution to optimum as may be required.

In the problem at hand, the MODI method will show that the optimum (minimum cost) solution has been obtained with the VAM and that no further improvement is possible (for further verification see Figure 20, page 29). If the optimum solution is not obtained with the VAM, then the MODI method would be applied until the optimum solution is obtained.

Auxiliary Rules. The preceding discussion considers what may be called the basic VAM. With practice many auxiliary rules can be developed, such as the following:

8. When the greatest difference is obtained at the same time in both a row and a column, and the square at the junction of that row and column has the algebraically largest cost or profit element, then the assignment is made at that square common to both the row and column. If the square at the junction does not have the algebraically largest cost or profit element, then make an assignment in either the row or column wherever the algebraically largest element exists.

9. When the greatest difference is obtained at the same time in two or more rows (or columns), then assign wherever the algebraically largest element exists in either row (or column).

These are only two of many auxiliary rules. It does not seem advisable to burden a relatively simple approximation method with too many auxiliary rules. Experience with a class of distribution-type problems will lead to possible modifications and shortcuts. The VAM is an approximation method for an initial solution that will usually yield a solution at least very close to the optimum. Hence a long list of involved rules seems out of order.

Degeneracy. Degeneracy can be detected when applying VAM. From the preceding discussion it can be seen that, when an assign-

From \ To	Chicago	Cleveland	Dayton	Minneapolis	Supply
Flint	−27	−23	−31	−69	150
Janesville	−10	−45	−40	−32	40
St. Louis	−30	−54	−35	−57	80
Demand	90	70	70	40	270 \ 270

Fig. 42. A Degenerate Problem

ment is made while applying VAM, either a row or column is fully utilized or satisfied with each assignment. Degeneracy is evident when both a row and a column are simultaneously fulfilled with one assignment. Consider a problem very similar to the one previously discussed but with slightly different rim conditions.

Note that the demand for Dayton and Minneapolis have been slightly changed. Proceeding with VAM, the initial assignment would be as shown in Figure 43.

	17	22	4	25		
To / From	Chicago	Cleveland	Dayton	Minneapolis	Supply	
Flint	−27	−23	−31	−69	150	4
Janesville	−10	−45	−40	−32 (40)	40	22
St. Louis	−30	−54	−35	−57	80	5
Demand	90	70	70	40	270 / 270	

Fig. 43. Initial VAM Assignment

It can be seen in Figure 43 that this initial assignment fulfills both a row and a column simultaneously. This indicates that the problem is degenerate. Proceeding with the VAM would yield subsequent assignments much similar to those of the preceding discussion. The VAM initial solution for the degenerate problem is shown in Figure 44.

The VAM initial solution is now obviously degenerate ($m+n-1$ assignments would mean 6 assignments—the problem has only 5 assignments). Degeneracy can now be resolved as indicated in the preceding discussion by the insertion of necessary zero stones.

Degeneracy can also be resolved during the VAM. When a row and a column are simultaneously fulfilled, a zero stone may, at that time, be inserted in an available square in either the row or column fulfilled. In the specific problem a zero stone could have been placed in either the second row or the fourth column as soon as the initial assignment was made.

To / From	Chicago	Cleveland	Dayton	Minneapolis	Supply
Flint	−27 (10)	−23 (70)	−31 (70)	−69	150
Janesville	−10	−45	−40	−32 (40)	40
St. Louis	−30 (60)	−54	−35	−57	80
Demand	90	70	70	40	270 / 270

Fig. 44. VAM Initial Solution

The optimum solution to this degenerate problem illustrates an interesting phenomenon of degenerate-type distribution problems. Two optimum solutions (in the sense that the zero stone can appear in either of two positions in the matrix) exist for this problem.

Although these two solutions in no way change the real shipments in the problem, it is interesting to note that the zero stone may appear in two (or possibly more) positions.

Summary. Vogel's approximation method offers a very useful and most efficient means of obtaining an initial solution for distribution-type problems. The VAM can in effect mean economical

To / From	Chicago $K_1 = -27$	Cleveland $K_2 = -23$	Dayton $K_3 = -31$	Minneapolis $K_4 = -49$	Supply
$R_1 = 0$ Flint	−27 (10)	−23 (70)	−31 (70)	−69	150
$R_2 = +17$ Janesville	−10 (0)	−45	−40	−32 (40)	40
$R_3 = -3$ St. Louis	−30 (60)	−54	−35	−57	80
Demand	90	70	70	40	270 / 270

Fig. 45. Optimum Solution—Degenerate Problem

To / From	$K_1 = -27$ Chicago	$K_2 = -23$ Cleveland	$K_3 = -31$ Dayton	$K_4 = -54$ Minneapolis	Supply
$R_1 = 0$ Flint	−27 (10)	−23 (70)	−31 (70)	−69	150
$R_2 = +22$ Janesville	−10	−45	−40	−32 (40)	40
$R_3 = -3$ St. Louis	−30 (60)	−54	−35	−57 (0)	80
Demand	90	70	70	40	270 / 270

Fig. 46. Another Optimum Solution—Degenerate Problem

hand solution to many problems heretofore solvable only with computing equipment. The usefulness of VAM will be further illustrated in succeeding chapters where it will be applied to distribution-type problems.

The VAM can be applied to distribution-type problems when the matrix is established and the rim conditions are balanced. The steps of the method are:

1. Determine the differences (absolute differences) between the two most (algebraically) maximum elements (cost or profit values) for each row and each column of the matrix.

2. Select the row or column with the greatest difference.

3. Assign as much as possible to the square with the most (algebraically) maximum element in that selected row or column.

4. Cross out the row or column completely utilized or satisfied by the assignment.

5. Redetermine the differences as may be necessary, but omit the row(s) and column(s) crossed out.

6. Repeat steps 2 through 5 until all assignments are made.

7. When all assignments have been made, then apply the MODI method to improve the solution to optimum as may be required.

Many supplementary or auxiliary rules have been developed, several of which are as follows:

8. When the greatest difference is obtained at the same time in both a row and a column, and the square at the junction of that row and column has the algebraically largest cost or profit element, then the assignment is made at that square common to both the row and column. If the square at the junction does not have the algebraically largest cost or profit element, then make an assignment in either the row or column wherever the algebraically largest element exists.

9. When the greatest difference is obtained at the same time in two or more rows (or columns), then assign wherever the algebraically largest element exists in either row (or column).

Degeneracy can be recognized and resolved when applying VAM in the following manner:

10. When a row and a column are simultaneously fulfilled with one assignment, the problem is degenerate. The degeneracy may be resolved at that time by inserting a zero stone in an available square in either the row or column.

Resolving degeneracy as in step 10 can be accomplished in most cases by placing the zero stone merely by inspection. However, often the zero stone ends up in a square where intuition or inspection would not normally place it.

Vogel's approximation method offers a very simple and easy routine that takes much of the work out of solving distribution problems. The VAM offers some interesting research possibilities. Research can be conducted to determine the mathematical basis for the VAM. It seems rational that such research can be successfully accomplished. Once a mathematical basis is developed, it may then be possible to apply it toward obtaining a better initial solution for the simplex method. In the next chapter, the simplex method is presented, and it will be seen then that any means of improving the initial solution would certainly reduce the time and cost of the simplex method.

MULTI-DIMENSIONAL DISTRIBUTION PROBLEMS

The distribution problems considered up to now have been two-dimensional problems. However, it is possible to encounter distribution-type problems in three and more dimensions. These multi-dimensional problems can only be solved by the more general method of mathematical programming; the simplex method (discussed in Chapter 3). This type of formulation and solution to distribution problems is very similar to going all around town to get to a destination when a short-cut (like the MODI method for two-dimensional distribution problems) is readily available.

An approximation method, involving the deviation of the cost elements from a weighted row and column average, has been developed by Dr. B. A. Galler.[16] This method has the potential of being better than the VAM for certain distribution problems. However, it is an approximation, and no techniques have been developed to improve upon this approximation. Experience with several problems indicates that this approximation yields a solution that is 90 per cent or better of the optimum solution. Actually a serious question arises here as to which solution is truly optimum, when the very best solution costs considerably more to obtain than the approximate one. Here both the solution and the expense to obtain it must be considered.

It may be well to consider how a third and a fourth dimension can be added to a distribution problem. The basic two-dimensional problem involved shipments between a number of origins and a number of destinations. This can be denoted by subscript notation, where

x_{ij} = the number of units shipped from origin i to destination j

A third dimension, various time periods, can be included where

x_{ijk} = number of units shipped from origin i to destination j in time period k

A fourth dimension can be included if the distribution system has intermediate assembly or warehouse locations. Then,

x_{ijkl} = number of units shipped from origin i to destination j in time period k via intermediate warehouse l

Still another dimension could be different items. Then,

x_{hijkl} = number of units of product h distributed from origin i to destination j in time period k via intermediate warehouse l

It becomes evident that the multidimensional aspect of distribution-type problems is certainly more than mere theory and has many possible applications.

The approximation solution to the multidimensional distribution

[16] Galler, *op. cit.* pp. 2–3. This work is based on the work of P. S. Dwyer, *op. cit.*

problem is based upon the general mathematical expression of the multidimensional distribution problem.

For a three-dimensional problem, the general formulation would be as follows. If we let

a_i = the supply in units at source i
b_j = the demand in units at destination j
d_k = the capacity in units at intermediate warehouse k
$i = (1, 2, \cdots, p_1)$ the sources
$j = (1, 2, \cdots, p_2)$ the destinations
$k = (1, 2, \cdots, p_3)$ the intermediate warehouses

$N = \sum_{i=1}^{p_1} a_i = \sum_{j=1}^{p_2} b_j = \sum_{k=1}^{p_3} d_k$ the grand total of the rim conditions

x_{ijk} = number of units shipped from source i to destination j via intermediate warehouse k
c_{ijk} = cost per unit to ship from source i to destination j via intermediate warehouse k

then the general form of the distribution problem would be to determine integers x_{ijk} that will minimize

$$\sum_{i=1}^{p_1} \sum_{j=1}^{p_2} \sum_{k=1}^{p_3} x_{ijk} c_{ijk} \tag{1}$$

subject to

$$\sum_{i=1}^{p_1} \sum_{j=1}^{p_2} x_{ijk} = d_k \tag{2}$$

$$\sum_{i=1}^{p_1} \sum_{k=1}^{p_3} x_{ijk} = b_j \tag{3}$$

$$\sum_{j=1}^{p_2} \sum_{k=1}^{p_3} x_{ijk} = a_i \tag{4}$$

These equations (each one of the last three actually represents an entire system of equations) can be rather easily interpreted as meaning:

(1) Minimize the distribution costs.

(2) Whatever is distributed from a source to a destination must equal the capacity of the intermediate warehouse.

(3) Whatever is distributed from a source via an intermediate warehouse to meet a demand must be equal to the demand.

(4) Whatever is distributed to various destinations via intermediate warehouses from a source must equal the supply at that source.

The approximation method then proceeds in the following steps:

1. Calculate the weighted deviates of each cost element. For the above problem, if we let c'_{ijk} = the weighted deviate, the formula for this calculation is

$$c'_{ijk} = c_{ijk} - \frac{1}{N^2}\left[\sum_{i=1}^{p_1}\sum_{j=1}^{p_2} a_i b_j c_{ijk} + \sum_{i=1}^{p_1}\sum_{k=1}^{p_3} a_i d_k c_{ijk} + \sum_{j=1}^{p_2}\sum_{k=1}^{p_3} b_j d_k c_{ijk}\right] + \frac{2}{N^3}\left[\sum_{i=1}^{p_1}\sum_{j=1}^{p_2}\sum_{k=1}^{p_3} a_i b_j d_k c_{ijk}\right]$$

2. Assign as much as possible either to the square containing the algebraic minimum of the deviates (when the problem involves costs to be minimized) or to the algebraic maximum of the deviates (when the problem involves profits to be maximized).

3. Cross out the row or column satisfied or utilized.

4. Repeat steps 2 and 3, neglecting those rows and columns crossed out, until all assignments have been made.

Except for the bulk of computation in step 1, this approximation method is a relatively simple one. Obviously this method is not too well suited to hand computation and has been developed and programmed for automatic machine computation. Experience with several problems indicates that this approximation method is superior to the VAM, particularly in multidimensional and more complex distribution problems.

The weighted deviates calculated by the above formula(s) actually represent the difference between that particular cost element (c_{ijk}) and the grand weighted average. The last four terms of the equation represent the weighted averages. The first three represent the weighted averages in each pair of the three dimensions. The very last term is much like a weighted average in all three dimensions.

The multidimensional aspect of distribution problems is one that should not be overlooked. The approximation method presented here will provide a suitable solution for these types of problems, particularly where the true optimum solution would take too long or where the available cost data are approximate or estimated. However, if required, this approximation can serve as an initial solution for solving a multidimensional distribution problem by the simplex method.

SUMMARY

Some of the most useful methods of mathematical programming for solving distribution-type problems have been presented here in an easy-to-understand manner. One can see in these methods the gradual development and refinement that has taken place with time. Research in the entire area of mathematical programming is progressing so rapidly and on so many fronts that improvements, refinements, and new methods may very soon supplant some of the methods discussed here. However, the MODI method will probably remain as a basic tool for solving the general class of two-dimensional distribution problems.

One should bear in mind that distribution-type problems are a very special example of mathematical programming and comprise a minor portion of the total variety of problems solvable by mathematical programming.

The mathematics for the most part has been purposely minimized in this chapter. The next chapter on the simplex method will gradually develop and explain the more general terminology and notation of mathematical programming.

3.

The Simplex Method

INTRODUCTION

The simplex method is the more general method of mathematical programming. It is not quite as easy as its name might imply and involves considerably more work than the distribution methods considered previously. The methods discussed previously were limited in that they can be applied only to distribution-type problems which comprise a small portion of the vast number of problems that can be solved by linear or mathematical programming.

The simplex method can best be described as a technique of matrix algebra, used to obtain the optimum values for variables related in a system of linear inequalities.[17] This description will be further seen through the examples in this chapter. The simplex method can be equally well applied to solving systems of simultaneous linear equations. Hence it can be counted among the several techniques and methods useful in solving problems of this type.

---

[17] Linear inequalities—expressions whose variables are all to the first power, and hence are linear. The relationships are generally not equations, but are usually restrictions or similar inequalities which do not usually define a single solution but rather many possible solutions. This will be seen more fully in the succeeding material.

The simplex method is generally credited to G. B. Dantzig, though the first attempt at a textbook-type coverage was that of Charnes, Cooper, and Henderson.[18] Many others have contributed to and extended the method and its various theorems and proofs; notable among these, in addition to the afore-mentioned authors, are Lemke, Orden, and Dorfman.[19]

The simplex method as it is presented here differs from the way preceding authors would present it, primarily in the terminology used. The presentation here is much more elementary and somewhat nonmathematical in order to accomplish the purpose of this text. No attempt will be made here to develop the proof of the simplex method or its various theorems for several reasons: first, it is unnecessary to comprehend the proof of a method in order to use it effectively (i.e.; one does not have to be a mechanical engineer to use an automobile); second, very adequate treatment has been given to the mathematical implications of the simplex method, notably by Dantzig[20] and Charnes and Cooper.

The basic simplex method will be presented via a simple manufacturing problem. The problem will be developed and solved in its entirety. Following the basic simplex method, the discussion develops the geometric interpretation of a linear programming problem and the simplex method. Degeneracy, various types of algebraic relationships, and simplifications are then discussed. A distribution problem is illustrated as it would be shown if it were to be solved by the simplex method. The dual linear programming problem and the modified simplex method are also presented toward the end of the chapter.

THE BASIC SIMPLEX METHOD

The basic simplex method is most easily developed via a relatively simple problem. Consider the following manufacturing problem:

A manufacturer wishes to determine how to produce two products (A and B) so as to realize the maximum total profit from the sale of the products.

---

[18] Charnes, Cooper, and Henderson. *An Introduction to Linear Programming,* John Wiley & Sons, 74 pp., 1953.

[19] See the bibliography for a partial listing of the works of these and other authors in this and associated areas.

[20] T. C. Koopmans, *Activity Analysis of Production and Allocation,* John Wiley & Sons, 1951.

Both products are made in two processes (I and II). It takes 7 hours in process I and 4 hours in process II to manufacture 100 units of product A. It requires 6 hours in process I and 2 hours in process II to manufacture 100 units of product B.

Process I can handle 84 hours of work, and process II can take 32 hours of work in the schedule period.

If the profit is \$11.00 per 100 units for product A and \$4.00 per 100 units for product B, then how much of each of products A and B should be manufactured to realize the maximum profit? It is assumed that whatever is produced can be sold and that the set-up time on the two processes is negligible.

In some respects this problem is very similar to the word problems given to students learning elementary algebra.

It is necessary to develop a mathematical model (formulation) of the problem. Essentially an answer is required in terms of units of the products to be manufactured. Therefore, if we let

$$x = \text{number of 100's of product } A$$
$$y = \text{number of 100's of product } B$$

then an expression for the manufacturing time on each of the two processes can be developed. Obviously the time consumed manufacturing the two products cannot exceed the total available time on the processes. Mathematically, this would be

$$\text{Process I:} \qquad 7x + 6y \leq 84$$
$$\text{Process II:} \qquad 4x + 2y \leq 32$$

Note that the $7x$ would be the time spent on process I in manufacturing product A, and the $6y$ would represent the time on process I required to manufacture product B. The time required to manufacture the two products must not exceed the total time; hence the less-than or equal-to ($\leq$) sign is employed. A similar explanation would apply for the second expression representing time spent on process II.

The purpose of solving this problem is to determine x and y such that the profit will be maximum. The profit (or objective function as it will be called) can then be written:

$$11x + 4y = \text{maximum}$$

Note that the $11x$ represents the total profit derived from the sale of product A, and the $4y$ the profit from product B.

The problem can now be stated mathematically as follows: Determine x and y such that

$$11x + 4y = \text{maximum} \tag{3.1}$$

subject to:

$$7x + 6y \leq 84 \tag{3.2}$$
$$4x + 2y \leq 32 \tag{3.3}$$

Obviously the values calculated for x and y must be positive in order to yield meaningful answers. Hence it is implicit in mathematical programming, and in the specific problem at hand, that

$$x \geq 0$$
$$y \geq 0$$

We will see later how this implicit requirement is met in the simplex method.

In order to apply the simplex method to the problem at hand, it is necessary to make equations of the two inequalities (3.2 and 3.3). This can be accomplished by the addition of slack variables as follows:

$$7x + 6y + W_1 = 84 \tag{3.4}$$
$$4x + 2y + W_2 = 32 \tag{3.5}$$

The symbol W will be used throughout this discussion for slack variables. A slack variable can be defined as any convenient positive number that causes equality to exist. In the above equations (3.4 and 3.5), the slack variable may be considered as idle equipment time. Therefore expression 3.4 can be explained:

$7x$ represents time required to produce product A.
$6y$ represents time required to produce product B.
W_1 represents idle equipment time.

Obviously then an equation can exist. There is nothing in the problem that says that the same amount of idle time must exist on both processes; hence the subscript is noted on the slack variables to eliminate confusion. If no gain or loss (profit or cost) is assumed for idle equipment time, then the profit or objective function (3.1) can be expanded to include the slack variables thus:

$$11x + 4y + 0 \cdot W_1 + 0 \cdot W_2 = \text{maximum} \tag{3.6}$$

Actually idle equipment costs (unabsorbed burden) can be included in the formulation. This will be illustrated later—for now no gain or loss is assumed for the slack variables.

The problem as it now stands is represented by a system of two equations (3.4 and 3.5) involving four variables (x, y, W_1, W_2) and an objective function (3.6). Mathematically this means that an infinite number of solutions exist for the problem. The simplex method offers a means of obtaining the very best answer most efficiently.

To facilitate handling the problem equations, they can be put into matrix form. In basic algebra, specifically determinants, it was found that systems of equations can be solved by working with the coefficients alone, and one does not need to rewrite the variables many times. This is somewhat similar to what will be done here. The two equations (3.4 and 3.5) in matrix form are shown in Figure 47.

	x	y	W_1	W_2
84	7	6	1	0
32	4	2	0	1

Fig. 47. Problem Equations in Matrix Form

Note that the first line represents equation 3.4, and the second line equation 3.5. Note also that the constants have been placed to the left of the equation.

The problem is now shown in a 2×4 matrix array [i.e., two rows (equations) and four columns (variables)].

As with the distribution methods, it is necessary to establish an initial solution. However, to illustrate the simplex method, the initial solution will be the worst possible or trivial solution. The worst possible or trivial solution for this problem would be to produce nothing, have all idle equipment time, and hence reap no profit. If nothing were produced, then all the available equipment time would be idle time, and the values for the variables would be:

$$x = 0$$
$$y = 0$$
$$W_1 = 84$$
$$W_2 = 32$$

This initial or trivial solution can be noted in the matrix array as in Figure 48.

		x	y	W_1	W_2
W_1	84	7	6	1	0
W_2	32	4	2	0	1

Fig. 48. Initial or Trivial Solution Shown in Matrix

Note that the slack variables have been placed to the left of the matrix (in what will be referred to as the stub) and may be read:

$$W_1 = 84$$
$$W_2 = 32$$

Since the variables x and y do not appear in the stub, they are by definition equal to zero.

The objective function (profit function 3.6) is included in the matrix array for reference. This will be used to evaluate the initial and succeeding solutions.

			11	4	0	0
			x	y	W_1	W_2
0	W_1	84	7	6	1	0
0	W_2	32	4	2	0	1

Fig. 49. Matrix including Objective Function

The objective function is written above the position of the variables, and the appropriate objective numbers are written to the left of the variables in the stub. At this point it will add to the clarity of the discussion if various parts of the matrix are named.

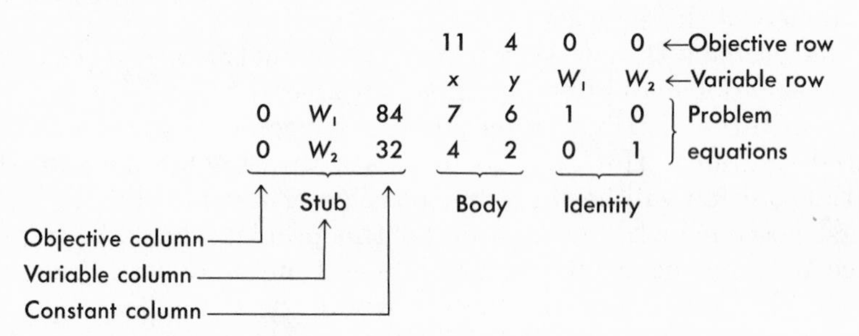

Fig. 50. Nomenclature of the Simplex Matrix

The solution stub of the matrix always contains the three columns. However, the body and identity may be considerably larger than two columns each, depending upon the particular problem.

To improve upon the initial (trivial) solution, some measure of improvement potential (much like water-square values in the MODI method) must be developed. This is accomplished in another row, an index row, that will be developed and placed below the matrix array.

Numbers appear in the index row under the constant column, body, and identity. They are developed from the formula:

Index number $= \sum$ (numbers in column) $\times$ (corresponding number in objective column)
$-$ (number in objective row at head of column)

The index row numbers for the problem at hand are calculated as follows:

Index number for constant column
$= \sum$ (numbers in column) $\times$ (numbers in objective column) $-$ (objective row number)
$= (84 \cdot 0) + (32 \cdot 0) - 0$
$= 0$

In the case of the constant column, a zero is implicit in the objective row.

Index number 1st column of body $= (7 \cdot 0) + (4 \cdot 0) - 11 = -11$
Index number 2nd column of body $= (6 \cdot 0) + (2 \cdot 0) - 4 = -4$
Index number 1st column of identity $= (1 \cdot 0) + (0 \cdot 0) - 0 = 0$
Index number 2nd column of identity $= (0 \cdot 0) + (1 \cdot 0) - 0 = 0$

The initial simplex matrix can now be written in its entirety (Fig. 51).

			11	4	0	0	
			x	y	W_1	W_2	
0	W_1	84	7	6	1	0	
0	W_2	32	4	2	0	1	
		0	−11	−4	0	0	←Index row

Fig. 51. Initial Simplex Matrix

It can be seen that the index row is merely the negative of the objective row. This will occur only when the objective column contains all zeros as in this problem.

Now that the problem is formulated and the initial simplex matrix is established, the simplex method can be used to improve the solution. The numbers in the index row give an indication of potential improvement in much the same manner as the water-square evaluations in the MODI method. The presence of negative numbers in the index row under either the body or identity indicates that the solution may be improved. The larger the negative number, the greater the potential improvement.

The greatest negative number in the index row occurs in the column headed by the variable x. This column will be designated as the key column. Actually any column containing a negative index number could be selected as the key column. However, this method will generally converge upon an optimum solution most rapidly when the column with the greatest negative index number is selected.

			11	4	0	0
			x	y	W_1	W_2
0	W_1	84	7	6	1	0
0	W_2	32	4	2	0	1
		0	−11	−4	0	0
			↑ Key column			

Fig. 52. Initial Simplex Matrix—Key Column Noted

The key column is circled for reference. This selection of the key column means that the variable x will be introduced into the solution, replacing one of the variables presently in the solution. The next step is to determine which variable will be replaced. The variable to be replaced will actually depend on which of the two problem equations limits or restricts x to the smallest amount. This is most conveniently accomplished as follows:

Divide each number in the constant column by the corresponding positive nonzero number in the key column. Compare the quotients obtained, and select the row with the smallest non-negative quotient.

In this problem the quotients would be:

$$\text{First row} \quad 84/7 = 12$$
$$\text{Second row} \quad 32/4 = 8$$

Since the second row has the smallest non-negative quotient, it can be designated as the key row and circled for reference.

The number common to both the key row and key column is designated as the key number.

The selection of the second row means that, in the next improved solution, the variable W_2 will be replaced by the variable x. This selection of the key row can be easily verified by examining the original problem relationships. Actually, since x shows the greatest possible improvement potential, one is interested in making x as

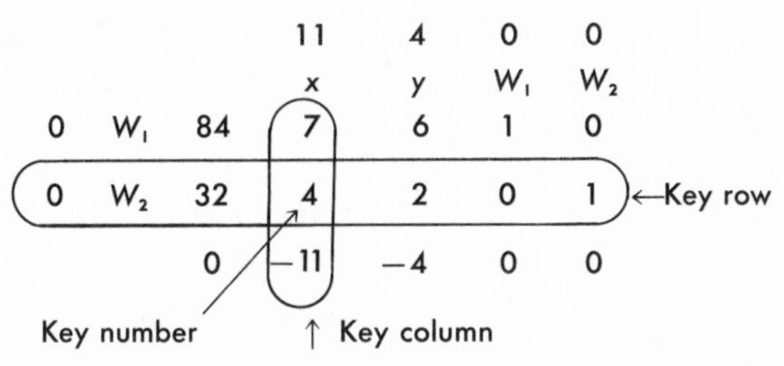

Fig. 53. Initial Simplex Matrix—Key Row and Key Number Noted

large as possible. The maximum value for x is determined by that relationship which limits x to the smallest value.

In the system

$$7x + 6y + W_1 = 84$$
$$4x + 2y + W_2 = 32$$

the variable x is limited to

(First equation) $x \leq 84/7 = 12$
(Second equation) $x \leq 32/4 = 8$

If x assumes a value larger than 8, then it will violate the second equation. In terms of the initial statement of the problem, a value for x greater than 8 requires more time on process II than the available 32 hours. Since this is impossible, x cannot be greater than 8 units. This corresponds to selecting as the key row that row with the smallest non-negative quotient.

With the selection of key column and key row accomplished, the simplex method can be employed to develop a new table representing an improved solution.

The first part of the new table to be developed may be called the main row. This main row appears in the same position as the key row of the preceding table, and is composed of the key row divided by the key number.

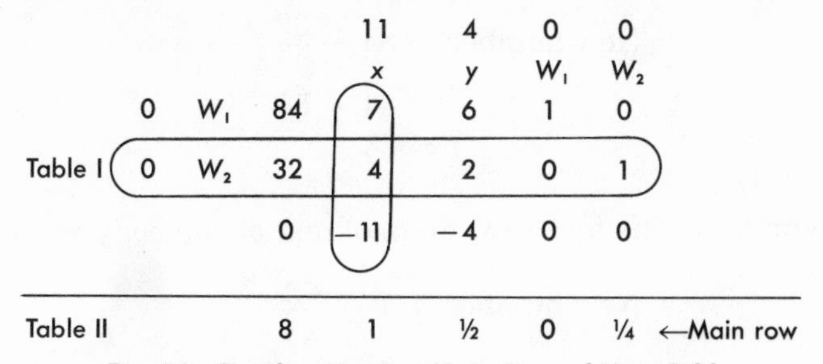

Fig. 54. Simplex Matrix—Main Row of New Table

Note that the variable and objective rows are not repeated in the new table merely to minimize the amount of writing. The variable and its objective number from the head of the key column are put in the stub of the main row replacing the variable and its objective number from the key row of the previous table. The remainder of the objective and variable columns in the stub are repeated in the new table.

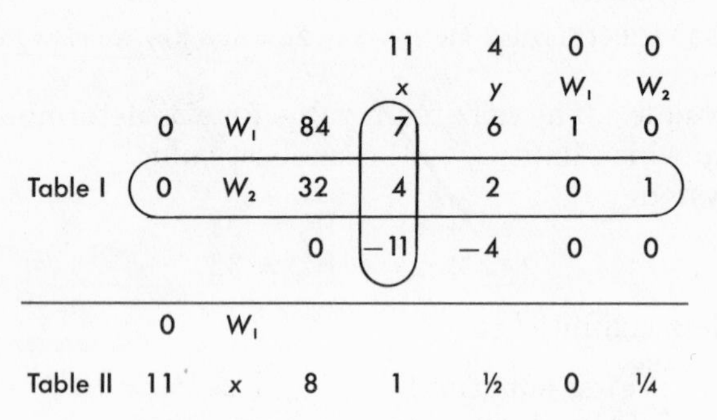

				11	4	0	0
				x	y	W_1	W_2
	0	W_1	84	7	6	1	0
Table I	0	W_2	32	4	2	0	1
			0	−11	−4	0	0
	0	W_1					
Table II	11	x	8	1	½	0	¼

Fig. 55. Simplex Matrix—Variables included in Second Table

All the remaining numbers in the new table, in the body, identity, constant column, and index row may be calculated by the following formula:

$$\text{New number} = \text{old number} - \frac{\begin{pmatrix}\text{corresponding number}\\ \text{of key row}\end{pmatrix} \times \begin{pmatrix}\text{corresponding number}\\ \text{of key column}\end{pmatrix}}{\text{key number}}$$

The number for the first row, constant column is calculated:

$$\begin{aligned}\text{New number} &= 84 - \frac{32 \times 7}{4}\\ &= 84 - 56\\ &= 28\end{aligned}$$

The number in the first row, first column of the body will be

$$\begin{aligned}\text{New number} &= 7 - \frac{4 \times 7}{4}\\ &= 0\end{aligned}$$

The number in the index row, constant column will be

$$\text{New number} = 0 - \frac{32 \times (-11)}{4}$$
$$= 88$$

When all the remaining numbers are calculated, then Table II will appear as in Figure 56.

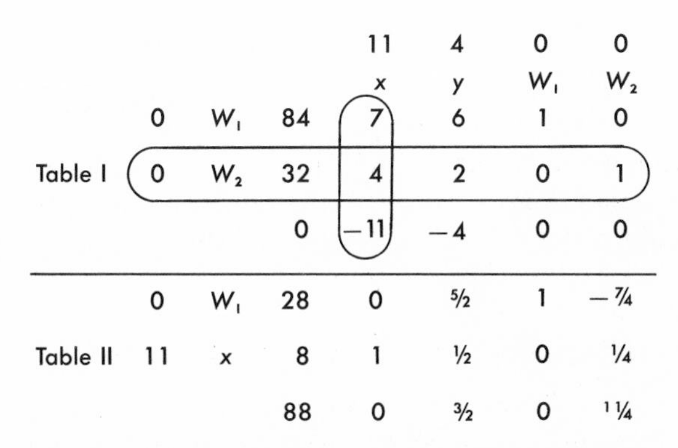

				11	4	0	0
				x	y	W_1	W_2
	0	W_1	84	7	6	1	0
Table I	0	W_2	32	4	2	0	1
			0	−11	−4	0	0
	0	W_1	28	0	5/2	1	−7/4
Table II	11	x	8	1	1/2	0	1/4
			88	0	3/2	0	11/4

Fig. 56. Simplex Matrix—First Iteration Completed

The index row of Table II (Fig. 56) contains all positive numbers under the body and identity. Therefore the solution contained in Table II is optimum. If any negative numbers remained in the index row under the body or identity, then the entire process would be repeated again until all the numbers were positive. The steps required to develop the improved solution (Table II) can be grouped together and are referred to mathematically as an iteration. If any negative numbers appeared in the index row of the second table, then another iteration would be accomplished to develop a third table in much the same manner as described when developing the second table. To iterate means to repeat; hence the same steps are repeated (the iterations are continued) as often as necessary to obtain an optimum solution.

The values of the variables can be obtained from the stub of Table II. The optimum solution is:

$$x = 8 \qquad W_1 = 28$$
$$y = 0 \qquad W_2 = 0$$

The variables x and W_1 appear in the stub with their value represented by the corresponding number in the constant column.

The variables y and W_2 are not listed in the stub and are, by definition, equal to zero. Any variable not in the stub is always equal to zero.

The above solution can easily be verified by substitution in the initial problem equations (3.4 and 3.5). The value of the objective function (i.e., the profit derived with the optimum solution) can also be obtained by substitution. The optimum profit is

$$\begin{aligned} 11x + 4y + 0 \cdot W_1 + 0 \cdot W_2 &= \text{maximum} \\ 11(8) + 4(0) + 0(28) + 0(0) &= \text{maximum} \\ \$88.00 &= \text{maximum} \end{aligned} \tag{3.6}$$

The value of the objective function can also be obtained directly from the simplex matrix array. The number in the index row and constant column represents the value of the objective function for the solution contained in the stub of the matrix array.

Economic significance can be attached to all the numbers in the index row. The general interpretation is as follows:

Index row under the body—the significance of these index numbers is very similar to the interpretation given the water-square evaluations in the MODI method.

A negative number indicates the algebraic increase that would occur in the objective function if one unit of the variable heading that column were introduced into the solution. Hence negative numbers here mean that further improvement in the solution is possible.

A positive number indicates the algebraic decrease that would occur in the objective function if one unit of the variable heading that column were introduced into the solution.

In Table II (Fig. 56), the index row number under the column headed by the variable y was $+3/2$. The above interpretation of this index number can be verified by substitution in the original problem equations. The second equation (3.5) will show the interpretation since it is the limiting expression.

$$4x + 2y + W_2 = 32 \tag{3.5}$$

if

$$y = 1$$
$$W_2 = 0$$

then,

$$4x + 2(1) + 0 = 32$$
$$x = \frac{30}{4} = 7\tfrac{1}{2}$$

This solution would yield the following profit:

$$\begin{aligned} 11x \quad + 4y \quad + 0 \cdot W_1 + 0 \cdot W_2 &= \text{profit} \\ 11(7\tfrac{1}{2}) + 4(1) \qquad\qquad &= \text{profit} \\ \$86.50 &= \text{profit} \end{aligned}$$

The profit from this solution is exactly \$1.50($\tfrac{3}{2}$) less than the optimum solution. Hence introducing one y into the solution reduces the value of the objective function by \$1.5(\$$\tfrac{3}{2}$).

Index row under the identity—a negative number here has the same significance as a negative number under the body of the matrix array.

A positive number can be thought of as potential "opportunity profit," or the amount of algebraic increase in the objective function if the restriction involving that variable could be relaxed by one unit.

This "opportunity profit" can be illustrated from Table II, Figure 56. The index number under the column headed W_2 is $1\tfrac{1}{4}$. If one more W_2 were available in the initial solution (i.e., if $W_2 = 33$ instead of 32 in Table I), then the objective function would be increased by $1\tfrac{1}{4}$ dollars. If

$$4x + 2y + W_2 = 33$$

and

$$y = 0$$
$$W_2 = 0$$

then

$$4x + 2(0) + 0 = 33$$
$$x = \frac{33}{4} \text{ or } 8\tfrac{1}{4}$$

The profit from this solution would be

$$\begin{aligned} 11(8\tfrac{1}{4}) + 4(0) &= \text{profit} \\ \$90.75 &= \text{profit} \end{aligned}$$

Note that this change has increased the profit function by \$2.75 or $1\tfrac{1}{4}$ dollars.

It is well to mention here that these interpretations for the index numbers hold true regardless of the size of the problem or type of objective function. Profit may not be the only objective; nevertheless, the same interpretation is valid. In the simplex method as with the MODI method, an optimum solution is obtained, and much information about alternative solutions is also provided.

The remaining numbers in the array also have an economic interpretation. The numbers within the body and identity of the array represent the marginal rate of exchange, at the solution represented in the stub, between the variable in the solution stub and the variable at the head of the column. For example, in the initial matrix array for the preceding problem, the first row was

			x	y	W_1	W_2
0	W_1	84	7	6	1	0

Each of the numbers in the body (columns x and y) and identity (columns W_1 and W_2) represent the marginal rate of exchange between the variable W_1 and the variables of the respective columns. In this case, seven units of W_1 are exchanged for one unit of x, six units of W_1 are exchanged for one unit of y, one unit of W_1 is exchanged for one unit of W_1, and zero units of W_1 are exchanged for one unit of W_2. This interpretation is completely general and applicable to any successive matrix array.

The interpretation for the first row of the second table in the preceding problem is as follows:

			x	y	W_1	W_2
0	W_1	28	0	$5/2$	1	$-7/4$

The marginal rate of exchange between x and W_1 is zero. One unit of y will be exchanged for $5/2$ units of W_1. Similarly, one unit of W_1 is exchanged for one unit of W_1. The negative sign on the $7/4$ indicates that W_1 will be increased by $7/4$ units for every unit of W_2 introduced into the solution.

In the case of a positive marginal rate of exchange, the variable in the stub of that row is decreased by the addition of one unit of the variable in that column. A negative marginal rate of exchange indicates the increase in the variable in the stub of that row with the addition of one unit of the variable in that column. This interpretation is completely general and permits rather rapid analysis of various alternative solutions, and the effect of changes in the basic data upon the solution(s).

Summary. This relatively simple problem has been used to illustrate the basic simplex method. It certainly seems in order now to collect the steps that were followed and present them in a concise manner. The basic simplex method can be summarized in the following steps:

1. Formulate the problem and the objective function.

2. Develop equations of the inequalities (this will be expanded in the succeeding discussion).

3. Develop the initial simplex matrix including the initial (trivial) solution and the index row numbers.

 a. The index row numbers in the initial matrix are calculated by the formula:

 Index number $= \sum$ (numbers in column) $\times$ (corresponding number in objective column) $-$ (number in objective row at head of column)

4. Select the key row—that row with the smallest non-negative quotient obtained by dividing each number of the constant column by the corresponding positive, nonzero number in the key column.

5. The key number is at the intersection of key row and key column.

6. Develop the main row of the new table.

$$\text{Main row} = \frac{\text{key row of preceding table}}{\text{key number}}$$

The main row appears in the new table in the same position as the key row of the preceding table.

7. Develop the remainder of the new table.

 a. The variable and its objective number at the head of the key column are written in the stub of the new table to the left of the main row. These replace the variable and objective number from the key row of the preceding table.

 b. The remainder of the variable and objective columns are reproduced in the new table exactly the same in the preceding table.

 c. The numbers of the new table, exclusive of the main row, are calculated by the formula:

$$\text{New number} = \text{old number} - \frac{\begin{pmatrix}\text{corresponding no.}\\ \text{of key row}\end{pmatrix} \times \begin{pmatrix}\text{corresponding no.}\\ \text{of key column}\end{pmatrix}}{\text{key number}}$$

8. Repeat steps 4 through 7c until all the index numbers (exclusive of the constant column) are positive.

9. The interpretation of the optimum solution is as follows:

 a. The solution appears in the stub. The variables and their respective values will be shown there. All variables that do not appear in the stub are equal to zero.

 b. The index row numbers can be interpreted as follows:

  (1) The number in the index row, constant column is the value of the objective function for the solution represented in the stub of the matrix.

(2) A negative number under the body or identity indicates the algebraic increase in the objective function if one unit of the variable at the head of that column were introduced into the solution.

(3) A positive number in the index row under the body of the matrix array represents the algebraic reduction in the objective function if one unit of the variable at the head of that column were introduced into the solution.

(4) A positive number under the identity has much the same meaning as in (3) above. However, it may also be thought of as representing "opportunity profit" or the amount of algebraic increase possible in the objective function if one more unit of the variable heading that column were available in the initial solution: i.e., if the restraint of the problem were relaxed by one unit.

c. The remaining numbers in the array represent the marginal rate of exchange between the variables in the row and column at the particular solution represented in the stub.

(1) A *positive* rate of exchange indicates the *decrease* in the variable in that row that results with the addition of one unit of the variable in that column.

(2) A *negative* rate of exchange indicates the *increase* in the variable in that row that results with the addition of one unit of the variable in that column.

It is well to re-emphasize here that only the basic rudiments of the techniques of problem formulation and the simplex method have been covered thus far. The remainder of this chapter will develop some of the refinements. However, the problem just presented does illustrate how the simplex method can be used to develop an optimum solution and at the same time provide useful information (in the index row numbers) about alternative courses of action.

VARIATIONS

The previous problem was solved to yield maximum profits. This section illustrates how the same problem may be solved for other objectives such as maximum machine utilization and maximum number of pieces produced.

Idle Equipment Costs Included. In the preceding problem, no gain or loss was associated with the slack variables W_1 and W_2 representing idle equipment time. Actually idle equipment time costs money, and this cost should, if possible, be included in the formulation. Let us assume the following idle equipment costs:

Process I = \$3.00 per hour
Process II = \$5.00 per hour

With this assumption, the problem relationships are:

$$7x + 6y + W_1 = 84 \qquad (3.4)$$
$$4x + 2y + W_2 = 32 \qquad (3.5)$$

and the objective is now

$$11x + 4y - 3W_1 - 5W_2 = \text{maximum} \qquad (3.7)$$

Note how the objective function now contains profit for the products and costs for the slack variables (idle equipment time).

It is not unusual for the reader to be confused at this point since the system (3.4 and 3.5) has remained unchanged but yet the objective function has been modified. The following simile should clarify the confusion.

The system (set of relationships) describes the boundaries of the problem or, let us say, describes the automobile. The objective function (one relationship) describes what is to be attained or represents a specific destination for the automobile. As we can guide an automobile to several different destinations, so likewise can several objectives apply to the same problem—conceivably each one yielding a different solution. In this respect, the system and objective are separate entities.

The problem as it now stands (equations 3.4, 3.5, and 3.7) can be put into matrix form and the initial simplex matrix developed.

			11	4	−3	−5
			x	y	W_1	W_2
−3	W_1	84	7	6	1	0
−5	W_2	32	4	2	0	1

Fig. 57. Problem Matrix including Idle Equipment Costs

Figure 57 illustrates the problem in matrix form with the objective row noted and the initial or trivial solution included in the stub.

The next step is to establish the index row numbers. This is where the difference between the two objective functions becomes very noticeable.

The index row numbers are calculated by the formula:

Index number $= \sum$ (numbers in the column) $\times$ (corresponding number in objective column) $-$ (number from objective row)

The index number for the constant column is

$$\text{Index number} = [84(-3) + 32(-5)] - 0 = -412$$

The remaining index numbers are calculated in a similar manner and appear as shown in Figure 58.

			11	4	−3	−5
			x	y	W_1	W_2
−3	W_1	84	7	6	1	0
−5	W_2	32	4	2	0	1
		−412	−52	−32	0	0

Fig. 58. Initial Simplex Matrix-Problem including Idle Equipment Costs

Note how the index row of this simplex array differs from that shown in Figure 51.

The same steps of the simplex method would be followed to solve the problem represented in Figure 58. The solution, however, will reflect the idle equipment costs assigned to the slack variables.

Maximum Number of Pieces Solution. The same problem can be rather simply solved for the maximum number of pieces. This type of solution would require an objective function that mathematically would be

$$x + y = \text{maximum}$$

and the entire problem can most simply be stated: Maximize

$$x + y \tag{3.8}$$

subject to

$$7x + 6y \leq 84 \tag{3.2}$$
$$4x + 2y \leq 32 \tag{3.3}$$

Exactly the same method as discussed earlier would be used to develop the initial simplex matrix array.

Figure 59 illustrates the initial simplex matrix for this problem.

			1	1	0	0
			x	y	W_1	W_2
0	W_1	84	7	6	1	0
0	W_2	32	4	2	0	1
		0	−1	−1	0	0

Fig. 59. Initial Simplex Matrix—Maximum Number of Pieces Objective

It can be seen that a tie exists between the two columns in the body of the matrix. They both have the greatest negative index number. In such tie situations, either column may be selected as the key column. This is a completely general rule. However it is interesting to see the result in the problem at hand. If one column is selected as the key column, three iterations are necessary to obtain the optimum solution. If the opposite choice is made, the problem can be solved in one iteration. Exactly the same solution is obtained except that more work is required with the one choice. No effective scheme has been devised to assist in selecting the key column in a tie situation. The situation of a tie between two rows for key row will be included in the discussion of degeneracy later.

Maximum Equipment Utilization Solution. The preceding problem can also be solved to maximize the equipment utilization. In terms of the variables of the problem, this objective is to minimize the idle equipment time, or mathematically,

$$W_1 + W_2 = \text{minimum}$$

The simplex method is an algebraically maximizing method and requires an objective function to equal maximum. This requirement can be met as follows:

Since $f(x) = \text{minimum}$ is equivalent to saying $-f(x) = \text{algebraically maximum}$, the objective function can be written

$$-W_1 - W_2 = \text{maximum}$$

The problem can then be stated: Maximize

$$-W_1 - W_2 \tag{3.9}$$

subject to

$$7x + 6y \leq 84 \tag{3.2}$$
$$4x + 2y \leq 32 \tag{3.3}$$

The initial simplex matrix array would then be as shown in Figure 60.

The simplex method would then yield a solution that will have

			0	0	−1	−1
			x	y	W_1	W_2
−1	W_1	84	7	6	1	0
−1	W_2	32	4	2	0	1
		−116	−11	−8	0	0

Fig. 60. Initial Simplex Matrix—Maximum Utilization Objective

an absolute minimum of idle equipment time. This solution incidentally may or may not be the same as the solution including idle equipment costs discussed previously.

These variations have been presented to illustrate the difference between the system and the objective function, as well as to give some slight insight into the possible types of objective functions.

The three variations of the initial problem have not been carried to their solutions in order that the interested reader may try his skill at using the simplex method. The solutions are presented in the succeeding discussion of the geometric interpretation of the problem and may easily be verified graphically there.

Short-cuts. It is probably apparent to the diligent reader by this time that several short-cuts are possible. These will be developed and explained here.

First it may be noted that a zero appears in the index row for columns whose variables appear in the stub of the matrix. This is a completely general statement and applies at any stage (iteration) of the solution to a problem.

It may be noted further that, for every variable in the stub, the column with that variable contains all zero numbers except that a "+1" appears at the junction of the row and column with the same variable. By the same token the key column appears in the succeeding table with a "+1" at the junction of the main row. The remainder of the column contains zeros.

In the formula used to calculate the numbers of a new table, it can be verified that, if a zero should appear in the key column, that row remains unchanged in the new table. Similarly, if a zero appears in the key row (and of course main row of the new table), then that column remains unchanged in the new table.

These short-cuts can be rather easily verified, and so they will not be proved here. However, these short-cuts materially reduce the iteration time. In most problems with the above short-cuts only 10 to 20 per cent of the numbers in the matrix must be calculated in any one iteration—a considerable savings in time and effort.

Checking the Work. One does not have to work with very many problems in mathematical programming until it becomes evident that a convenient means for checking the work is required. In relatively small problems it is not too difficult to double-check each calculation. As the problems become larger and involve more iterations, this means of checking for errors adds to the tedium and soon escapes human capabilities. Then too, while it is possible to double-check for correct numbers, it is extremely easy to run into number transposition errors.

Two methods are available for detecting errors. The first method involves checking the index row numbers after each iteration. The index row numbers for the second and succeeding tables are calculated by the formula used to calculate the other numbers in the matrix array. The checking scheme involves calculating the index numbers in the same manner as they are initially established and comparing the results. Consider the matrix array of the previous problem as an example.

				11	4	0	0
				x	y	W_1	W_2
Table I	0	W_1	84	7	6	1	0
	0	W_2	32	4	2	0	1
			0	−11	−4	0	0
	0	W_1	28	0	5/2	1	−7/4
Table II	11	x	8	1	1/2	0	1/4
			88	0	3/2	0	1 1/4

Fig. 61. Simplex Solution to a Manufacturing Problem

The index row numbers in Table II were calculated by the formula:

$$\text{New number} = \text{old number} - \frac{\begin{pmatrix}\text{corresponding number}\\ \text{of key row}\end{pmatrix} \times \begin{pmatrix}\text{corresponding number}\\ \text{of key column}\end{pmatrix}}{\text{key number}}$$

It is possible to check these numbers by the formula used originally to establish the index numbers in the initial simplex matrix (Table I).

$$\text{Index number} = \sum (\text{number in column}) \times (\text{corresponding number in objective column}) - (\text{objective number at head of column})$$

The check calculation for the index number in the constant column (Table II) is

$$\begin{aligned}\text{Index number} &= [(28)(0) + (8)(11)] - 0 \\ &= 88\end{aligned}$$

The check calculation for the index number in the first column of the body (column containing x) is

$$\begin{aligned}\text{Index number} &= [(0)(0) + (1)(11)] - 11 \\ &= 0\end{aligned}$$

The same check calculation is continued for each index number. If an error is detected, then the numbers in that column are rechecked.

This check routine has one big limitation aside from the fact that it becomes rather cumbersome for relatively large matrices. That limitation lies in the fact that an error in a row where the number in the objective column is zero (row one of Table II in Fig. 61, for example) can go undetected. Obviously this check routine is in reality only a partial check.

The second, and better, means of checking for errors in the work is with the use of a check column. This method permits a rapid and convenient means of error detection. Again consider the previous problem as an example.

			11	4	0	0
			x	y	W_1	W_2
0	W_1	84	7	6	1	0
0	W_2	32	4	2	0	1
		0	−11	−4	0	0

Fig. 62. Initial Simplex Matrix

The check column can be added to the right of the matrix array. The numbers in the check column are established as the algebraic sum of all the numbers in a row including the constant column, body, and identity of the matrix.

The check column properly established for the above initial simplex matrix is as shown in Figure 63.

			11	4	0	0	
			x	y	W_1	W_2	ck
0	W_1	84	7	6	1	0	98
0	W_2	32	4	2	0	1	39
		0	−11	−4	0	0	−15

Fig. 63. Initial Simplex Matrix including Check Column

The check column has been set off from the matrix array so as not to be confused with any of the other columns in the matrix. Note that a check number is established for each row including the index row.

When the check column is once properly established, it is handled in the same manner as any other column in the matrix array. Of course, it is meaningless to consider the check column as a possible candidate when selecting the key column. If the check column has been properly established, and no errors have occurred in the iteration process, the numbers in the check column will always equal the algebraic summation of the number in the respective rows. The check column for the above problem would be handled as any other column in the matrix array, and the complete problem array would be as shown in Figure 64.

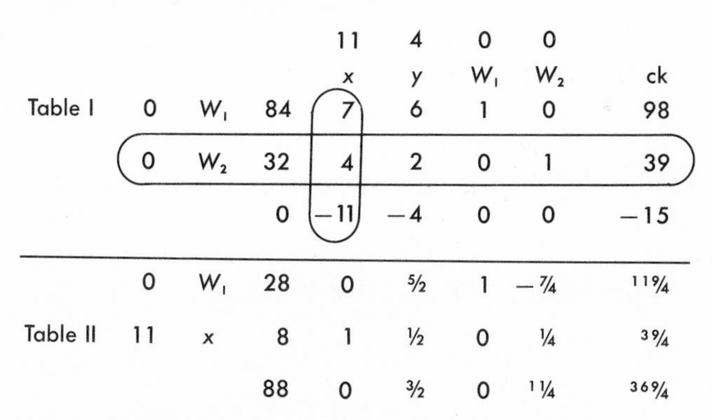

				11	4	0	0	
				x	y	W_1	W_2	ck
Table I	0	W_1	84	7	6	1	0	98
	0	W_2	32	4	2	0	1	39
			0	−11	−4	0	0	−15
	0	W_1	28	0	5/2	1	−7/4	119/4
Table II	11	x	8	1	1/2	0	1/4	39/4
			88	0	3/2	0	11/4	369/4

Fig. 64. Simplex Solution with Check Column

The numbers in the check column would be calculated in the same manner as the other numbers in the corresponding rows. The check-column number is then compared with the algebraic sum of the numbers in the row. If they tally, then the work is almost certainly error-free.

This method of checking the work for errors, although it does add another column to the matrix array, is much more efficient and requires less work than the first method described. In addition, the use of the check column affords a complete check of all the work, and not merely a partial check as with the first method discussed. It does not require too much experience before one grasps the importance and necessity of using a check column.

It is well to mention here that a check row can be established in much the same manner as the check column. This too offers a complete check of the work. The simplex matrix array always contains more columns than rows. Therefore, the check column is more efficient since it will contain fewer check sums than a check row. Then, too, a check row can be easily confused with the other rows of the array, whereas a check column is rather easily set apart from the array.

Of course, as Charnes and Cooper[21] point out, the all-important check though it may seem trite is in assessing the resulting solution(s) in terms of its meaningfulness and practicability as a course of action to the problem at hand. Mathematical programming work, regardless of how accurate, is useless unless the results can be presented to management as a realistic course of action. This will be further amplified in the applications presented later in the text.

GEOMETRIC INTERPRETATION

The preceding manufacturing problem can be quickly and easily solved graphically. The geometric interpretation of a mathematical (linear) programming problem and the simplex method will be developed here via the same manufacturing problem.

The problem formulation is: Maximize

$$11x + 4y \tag{3.1}$$

subject to

$$7x + 6y \leq 84 \tag{3.2}$$
$$4x + 2y \leq 32 \tag{3.3}$$

If the two relationships 3.2 and 3.3 are considered as equations,

$$7x + 6y = 84 \tag{3.2.1}$$
$$4x + 2y = 32 \tag{3.3.1}$$

they may be plotted as two straight lines as shown in Figure 65.

[21] Charnes, Cooper, Henderson, *op. cit.*, p. 18.

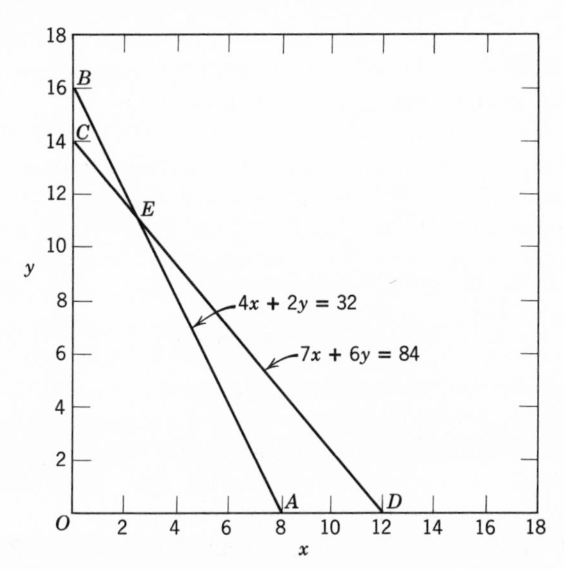

Fig. 65. Problem Equations Graph

Line AEB can be defined as the locus of points satisfying the equation

$$4x + 2y = 32$$

Since the actual problem relationship is an inequality (a less-than-or-equal-to relationship), then an area of possible solutions exists. The area $AEBO$ is the area of possible solutions to the inequality.

$$4x + 2y \leq 32$$

Similarly, the line DEC represents the locus of points satisfying the equation

$$7x + 6y = 84$$

and the area $DECO$ represents the locus of points satisfying the inequality

$$7x + 6y \leq 84$$

The area that is common to both inequalities, area $AECO$, represents the locus of points satisfying the system

$$7x + 6y \leq 84$$
$$4x + 2y \leq 32$$

and hence contains the possible solutions to the problem. Note how the ordinate and abscissa and the two relationships define the boundaries of the problem. Point E is, of course, the simultaneous solution to the two equations.

This graph verifies an earlier statement that the problem has an infinite number of possible solutions. Actually what the simplex method does is to find the very best (most maximum profit) solution. This can be accomplished graphically.

The objective (profit) function

$$11x + 4y = \text{maximum}$$

defines (geometrically) a series of lines with a $-11/4$ slope. The negative sign describes a straight line that is directed down to the right and up to the left. The $11/4$ means that, for every 11 divisions vertically, the line is offset 4 divisions horizontally. Let us backtrack a moment and see how this was obtained.

One of the general forms of a two-variable linear equation is

$$y = mx + b$$

where $\left.\begin{matrix} x \\ y \end{matrix}\right\}$ = the variables

m = the slope of the line

b = the y intercept (value of y when $x = 0$)

The above objective function can be placed into this general form; thus:

$$11x + 4y = \text{maximum}$$

$$y = -\frac{11}{4}x + \frac{\text{maximum}}{4}$$

$$m = -\frac{11}{4}$$

The profit function is then represented by a family of straight lines (a number of parallel lines) with a $-11/4$ slope.

If the profit function (one of these lines with a $-11/4$ slope) were superimposed on the graph in Figure 65 (Fig. 66), then the line could be interpreted as a locus of points all of which yield identically the same profit.

The objective function in the form

$$y = -\frac{11}{4}x + \frac{\text{maximum}}{4}$$

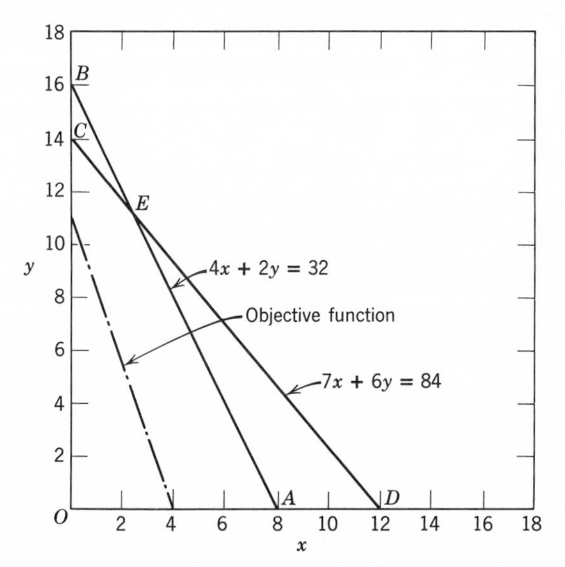

Fig. 66. Problem Graph—Objective Function Superimposed

indicates that, to obtain the maximum value of the function (maximum profit), the line must be as far from the origin as possible and still satisfy the problem relationships (3.2 and 3.3). This is shown graphically in Figure 67.

The profit function contacts the area of possible solutions where

$$x = 8$$
$$y = 0$$

by substitution; in the profit function, this solution yields a profit of \$88. Since the objective function line is as far from the origin as possible and still contains a point in *AECO,* namely point *A,* this is the optimum (maximum profit) solution. This compares exactly with the solution obtained previously via the simplex method.

This problem was rather easily solved graphically. However the graphical solution does not yield as much information as the simplex solution. Then, too, the solution is only as accurate as the graph construction. Two or three variable problems can usually be solved graphically. However, when a problem contains four or more variables, a graphical solution is impossible, though the same general concept holds true.

Certainly one cannot attempt to visualize this in more than three dimensions. Let it suffice to say that a linear programming prob-

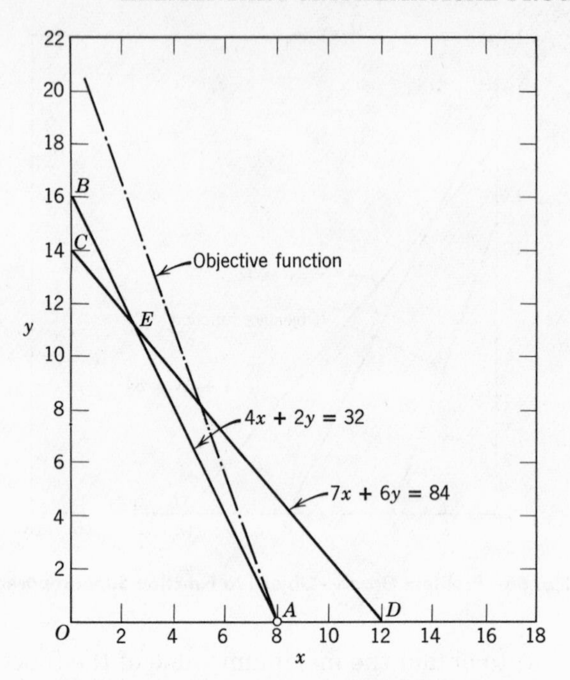

Fig. 67. Optimum Solution—Maximum Profit

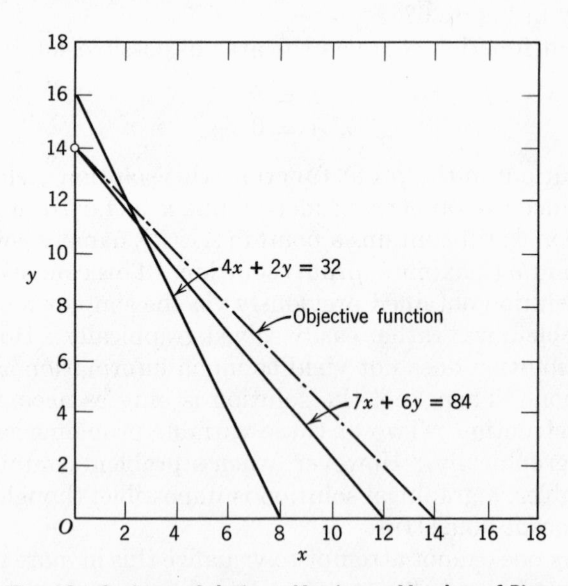

Fig. 68. Optimum Solution—Maximum Number of Pieces

lem in four or more unknowns is similar to a two- or three-variable problem, in that the system of relationships encloses a possible solutions space and the simplex method seeks an extreme point with the objective function.[22]

The graph (Fig. 65) can rather easily yield the solution for the maximum number of pieces and the maximum equipment utilization. The objective function for maximum number of pieces was

$$x + y = \text{maximum}$$

which describes a family of lines with a (-1) slope.

The optimum solution for maximum number of pieces is

$$x = 0$$
$$y = 14$$

This is the same solution that can be obtained with the simplex method.

The solution with minimum equipment idle time would be simply the simultaneous solution to the two equations:

$$7x + 6y = 84$$
$$4x + 2y = 32$$

where

$$x = 2.4$$
$$y = 11.2$$

This too would be obtained via the simplex method using the objective function

$$-W_1 - W_2 = \text{maximum}$$

The geometric interpretation of a mathematical programming problem is of interest in understanding the simplex method. Relatively simple two- and three-variable problems can most easily be solved graphically; however, the simplex method offers a completely general means of solving mathematical programming problems of any size with any number of variables.

DEGENERACY

Degeneracy, as previously discussed with the MODI method, can also be encountered in the simplex method. However, it is not

[22] For a complete mathematical discussion of this concept see Charnes, Cooper, Henderson, *op. cit.,* Part II, pp. 41–74.

quite as easily resolved. Degeneracy occurs either when the problem begins to cycle and never reaches optimum or when the problem collapses (one of the variables disappears) before an optimum has been obtained. This can, of course, happen as a result of errors, but it can also occur as a result of the problem itself.

More specifically, degeneracy can be recognized in the simplex method when selecting the key row. If a tie occurs between two or more rows (rows having the same smallest non-negative quotient of the constant column number divided by the corresponding positive, non-zero key column number), then the problem is degenerate. The degeneracy is resolved as follows:[23]

1. Divide each element in the "tied" rows by its key column number.

2. Compare the ratios so obtained term by term (column by column) from left to right first in the identity and then in the body.[24]

3. The tie is broken when the ratios are unequal.

4. Select as the key row that row with the algebraically smaller ratio.

Consider a degenerate problem to see how the above applies (Fig. 69).

			7	6	8	4	3	5	0	0	0	0
			x_1	x_2	x_3	x_4	x_5	x_6	W_1	W_2	W_3	W_4
0	W_1	100	5	−2	3	10	−1	−4	1	0	0	0
0	W_2	50	4	0	5	−1	−3	5	0	1	0	0
0	W_3	20	3	1	−3	0	0	0	0	0	1	0
0	W_4	40	8	4	4	3	6	5	0	0	0	1
		0	−7	−6	−8	−4	−3	−5	0	0	0	0

Fig. 69. A Degenerate Problem

The key column has been noted in the above array. The possible candidates for key row are rows 1, 2, and 4. Row 3 cannot be selected because the key column number is negative. The quotients are:

[23] Charnes, Cooper, Henderson, *op. cit.*, pp. 20–25. This is the basis for the above discussion and includes a very comprehensive appraisal of the entire scope of the problem of degeneracy.

[24] The procedure for resolving degeneracy, as presented in Charnes and Cooper, indicates comparison of ratios left to right in the array. However, the simplex matrix is organized by them with the identity to the left of the body. Hence their rule is modified to meet the organization of the matrix array as used here.

Row 1 $100/3 = 33\frac{1}{3}$
Row 2 $50/5 = 10$
Row 4 $40/4 = 10$

Hence a tie exists between the second and fourth rows. If the wrong row is selected as the key row, the possibility exists that the variable in the stub of the other tied row may permanently disappear (equal zero). The problem may then begin to cycle or continue indefinitely without attaining an optimum solution.

The tied rows must be divided by their key column number and the ratios compared. The comparison is as follows:

Column W_1 (first column of identity):
Row 2-0
Row 4-0

Column W_2
Row 2-$\frac{1}{5}$
Row 4-0

The tie is broken in the W_2 column, and row 4 becomes the key row for this matrix array, since it has the algebraically smaller of the two ratios.

In the succeeding simplex table it can be noted that the variable W_2 will become zero, but the danger of the problem cycling or collapsing has been eliminated by following the degeneracy rule. The above rules are completely general and apply equally well, regardless of the size of the array, and at any iteration of the problem, not only in the initial array as illustrated above.

Multiple degeneracy is evident when a tie occurs among more than two rows when selecting the key row. This condition is also resolved by the above degeneracy rules.

Degeneracy does not occur too frequently, and multiple degeneracy occurs even less frequently. However, a degenerate condition must be recognized and resolved correctly, or much work and effort can go to waste. Degeneracy is most apt to occur in problems where the constant column contains several zeros.

A question quite naturally arises here: "What happens if a tie exists between two or more columns when selecting the key column?" The answer is relatively simple. A tie between two columns is not a degenerate situation. Either one of the columns may be arbitrarily designated as the key column. The choice may affect the number of iterations but not the final result. A choice could be made by selecting that column that would have the smallest quotient in the selection of the key row. This, however, does not necessarily guarantee a minimum number of iterations to the solution.[25]

In general, then, when a tie occurs between two or more columns, any one may be selected as the key column. In the previous problem, where the objective was maximum number of pieces, such a tie existed. One choice led to the optimum solution in one iteration, whereas the other required three iterations to obtain the same optimum solution. In fact, the choice determined by the smallest quotient in selecting the key row is the choice that requires three iterations. This would seem to nullify the idea of carefully selecting the key column in such a tie situation.

TYPES OF RELATIONSHIPS

Up to now, only one type of relationship, namely the restriction, has been considered. While restrictions are the type of relationship most often encountered in mathematical programming problems, it is possible to have requirements, approximations, and equations in certain problems.

Restrictions are represented by the less-than-or-equal-to sign ($\leq$) and represent things or groups of events that may not exceed a given limitation.

Requirements are represented by the greater-than-or-equal-to sign ($\geq$) and represent things or groups of events that must be at least of a certain minimum (usually non-zero) value.

Approximations are represented by the approximately-equal-to sign ($\cong$) and represent things or groups of events that must be close to but not necessarily exactly equal to some value.

Equations are, of course, represented by the equal sign ($=$) and represent usually groups of events that must equate exactly to a given value.

Each of the preceding relationships requires slightly different handling in order to fit into the simplex matrix array. In general, all the inequality relationships are made into equations in preparation for the simplex method. Examples of the preceding will be illustrated, and several additional facts about the simplex matrix will be indicated.

[25] Charnes, Cooper, and Henderson, *op. cit.*, p. 15.

Restrictions. Restrictions are most easily handled. In fact, the problems discussed up to now have involved only restrictions. Consider the following example.

$$7x + 6y \leq 84$$

This restriction is ready for the simplex matrix by merely adding a slack variable:

$$7x + 6y + W_1 = 84$$

The slack represents the unused or unallocated portion of the 84 units. The real variables x and y appear in the body of the matrix, and the slack variable appears in the identity.

Requirements. Requirements must be handled in a slightly different manner. Consider the requirement

$$5x + 2y \geq 15$$

An equation will result if a slack variable is subtracted:

$$5x + 2y - W_2 = 15$$

The slack variable W_2 represents the amount of overage or the amount by which $5x + 2y$ exceeds 15.

This relationship cannot be put into the simplex matrix array in this form. The slack variable cannot fit in the identity because it is required that the identity be a positive unit diagonal array. In other words, the identity must be square (same number of columns as rows) and must be composed of all zeros except for a diagonal of positive ones. The variable W_2 would show a -1 in the matrix array; hence it cannot appear in the identity.

If the above relationship were multiplied by -1, it would then be

$$-5x - 2y + W_2 = -15$$

This permits the slack variable W_2 to appear in the identity. However the -15 cannot appear in the constant column since it is required that all the numbers in the constant column be positive. This positive requirement on the constant column numbers insures that all variables are greater than or equal to zero.

If we return to the relationship in the form

$$5x + 2y - W_2 = 15$$

then all that is required is a candidate for the identity. A candidate can be had in an artificial variable. It is possible to add an artificial variable to the preceding expression yielding

$$5x + 2y - W_2 + U_1 = 15$$

where U_1 is an artificial variable. (The symbol U will be used throughout the text to distinguish artificial variables from other variables.) This expression can then be put into the simplex matrix array. The real variables x and y and the slack variable W_2 will appear in the body, with the artificial variable U_1 in the identity. The artificial variable is merely a computational device that permits certain relationships to be included in the simplex method.

The artificial variable was included after equality existed in the relationship. Consequently, none of the artificial variable is wanted in an optimum solution. To assure that the artificial variable is driven to zero, we may assign an arbitrarily large cost to this variable in the objective function. This cost may be $-M$ (the same $-M$ as was used in the distribution methods previously discussed), defined as so prohibitively large that it dominates all else in the problem. This will make the initial solution (involving the variables of the identity) very costly, but will assure that all artificial variables will be zero in any optimum solution. No attempt is usually made to attach any economic significance to artificial variables, since they are of value only to the solution technique and not to the real problem.

Requirements are then readied for the simplex method by subtracting a slack variable to make an equation and then adding an artificial variable to have a candidate for the identity.

Approximations. Approximation relationships are not encountered as often as the other types of relationships. Consider the approximation

$$6x + 5y \cong 50$$

This can be prepared for the simplex method by both adding and subtracting slack variables:

$$6x + 5y - W_3 + W_4 = 50$$

The two slack variables permit $6x + 5y$ to be either smaller or larger than 50. The slack variable W_3 actually represents the amount by which $6x + 5y$ exceeds 50, and the slack variable W_4 actually represents the amount by which $6x + 5y$ is less than 50.

It is logical that we should try to minimize the value of the slack variables so that $6x + 5y$ will be as close as possible to 50 without necessarily making it exactly equal to 50.

This can be accomplished in the objective function by assigning a -1 to both slack variables (i.e.; the objective function may be $ax + by - W_3 - W_4 =$ maximum, where a and b are the unit profit or cost for x and y, respectively).

The relationship can now be included in a simplex matrix with the real variables x and y and the slack variable W_3 appearing in the body, and the slack variable W_4 appearing in the identity.

Equations. Equations may be encountered occasionally and are rather easily handled. In an equation, all that is lacking is a variable for the identity, and consequently for that relationship in the initial solution stub. This can be had by including an artificial variable. Consider the equation

$$3x + 4y = 100$$

This is ready for the simplex method by adding an artificial variable,

$$3x + 4y + U_1 = 100$$

and, of course, a $-M$ cost is assigned to the artificial variable U_1 in the objective function.

Summary. We have seen how four types of relationships are prepared for the simplex matrix array. Consider a hypothetical problem involving three of those relationships in a system.

Restriction:	$7x + 6y \leq 84$	Maximize $ax + by$ (a and
Requirement:	$5x + 2y \geq 15$	b are unit costs or profits
Approximation:	$6x + 5y \cong 50$	for x and y respectively)

The above system prepared for the simplex matrix array would then be: Maximize

$$ax + by + 0 \cdot W_1 + 0 \cdot W_2 - W_3 - W_4 - MU_1$$

subject to

$$\begin{aligned} 7x + 6y + W_1 \qquad\qquad &= 84 \\ 5x + 2y - W_2 + U_1 &= 15 \\ 6x + 5y - W_3 + W_4 &= 50 \end{aligned}$$

and the 3×7 matrix array is then as shown in Figure 70.

		a	b	0	−1	0	−M	−1
		x	y	W_2	W_3	W_1	U_1	W_4
W_1	84	7	6	0	0	1	0	0
U_1	15	5	2	−1	0	0	1	0
W_4	50	6	5	0	−1	0	0	1

Fig. 70. Initial Matrix Array

This system of three relationships can be represented graphically and solved rather easily with the graph. Figure 71 illustrates the system and can be interpreted as follows:

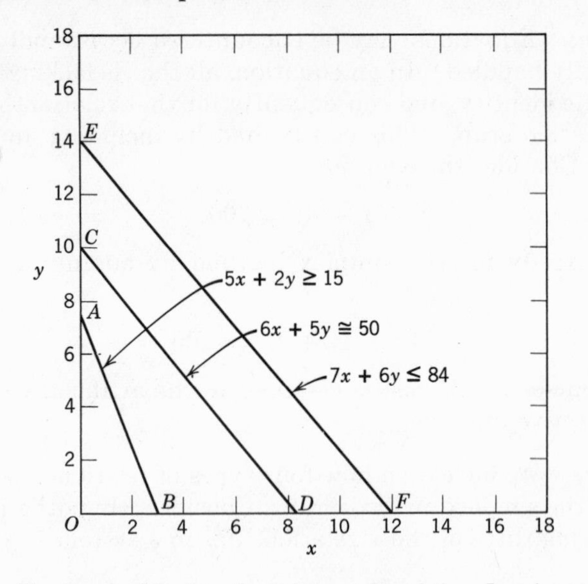

Fig. 71. Graph of System Containing a Restriction, Requirement, and an Approximation

The ordinate forms one boundary and the abscissa another boundary to the area of possible solutions. These lines represent the relationships

$$x \geq 0$$
$$y \geq 0$$

which are implicit in the linear programming problem.

Line AB represents the locus of points satisfying the relationship.

$$5x + 2y = 15$$

The area to the right of line AB and bounded by line AB and the ordinate and abscissa represents the locus of points satisfying the relationship

$$5x + 2y \geq 15$$

Line CD represents the locus of points satisfying the relationship

$$6x + 5y = 50$$

The area to both sides of line CD represents the locus of points satisfying the relationship

$$6x + 5y \cong 50$$

Line EF represents the locus of points satisfying the relationship

$$7x + 6y = 84$$

Area EFO represents the locus of points satisfying the relationship

$$7x + 6y \leq 84$$

In this problem then the area $AEFB$ represents the locus of points satisfying all three of the relationships. The problem can be solved graphically by superimposing the objective function on the graph as previously indicated.

SIMPLIFICATIONS

The simplex method is somewhat tedious, and so it makes good sense to strive for formulations as small and efficient as possible. There are basically two techniques that may be employed to eliminate rows and/or columns in the simplex matrix array. They are:

1. Elimination of redundant expressions and variables.
2. Algebraic substitution.

These simplification techniques will be explained via illustrative examples.

Redundant Expressions. One of the prime characteristics of mathematical programming problems is the presence of more variables than number of expressions. Many problems will possess this characteristic. However, occasionally a problem will be encountered possessing more relationships than variables. This usually indicates the presence of redundant expressions. Consider a problem represented by the following formulation:

$$x_3 + x_4 \leq 10 \quad (1)$$
$$x_1 + x_2 \leq 20 \quad (2)$$
$$x_3 + x_4 \leq 15 \quad (3)$$
$$3x_3 + 2x_4 \leq 52 \quad (4)$$
$$4x_1 + 3x_2 \leq 52 \quad (5)$$
$$2x_2 + 3x_4 \leq 26 \quad (6)$$
$$x_1 + 2x_3 \leq 52 \quad (7)$$

In all, the problem is represented by seven relationships combining only four real variables. To solve the problem in this form would require a 7 × 11 matrix array (seven rows and eleven columns or seven relationships combining the four real variables and seven slack variables). This is the reverse of the usual formulation in mathematical programming because ordinarily the number of real variables exceeds the number of relationships. There is every possibility then that one or more of these relationships are redundant or unnecessary.

Inspection of the seven relationships will show which ones are the truly limiting expressions for the four variables. For example: It can be observed that relation 1 nullifies relation 3. Similarly, if relation 2 is multiplied by the number 3, then relation 5 nullifies relation 2. Finally, relation 1 nullifies relation 4. Now, since x_1 is limited to a maximum of 13 by relation 5, and x_3 is limited to a maximum of 10 by relation 1, then relation 7 is nullified. This means that relationships (2), (3), (4), and (7) are redundant limitations, and the problem can be adequately expressed by the system:

$$x_3 + x_4 \leq 10$$
$$4x_1 + 3x_2 \leq 52$$
$$2x_2 + 3x_4 \leq 26$$

This system will require a 3 × 7 matrix array (three rows and seven columns or three relationships combining the four real variables and three slack variables). In terms of the quantity of numbers in the array, the simplification by elimination of redundant expressions reduces the size of the matrix to approximately one quarter of its original size.

In general, whenever the number of expressions is the same or exceeds the number of real variables, the chances are that one or more of the expressions are redundant and can be thrown out. However, it is well to note here that the type of relationship must be carefully considered. In fact, it often pays to check the relationships for redundancy and also for practicability. An error in formulation may have a requirement that a variable be of a size somewhat larger than the limitation imposed by another restriction. In general, however, the major portion of mathematical programming problems will rarely present more expressions than variables.

Redundant Variables. Redundant variables can be recognized when the initial simplex matrix is established. A variable and its entire column in an array can be thrown out when two or more columns in the array are identical, element for element, except for the objective number. For two identical columns in the array, it can be verified (via the formula used to calculate the new numbers in a new table) that the two columns will always remain the same. This means that, if the variable in either column enters a solution, it will be that variable with the more algebraically maximum objective number. The other variable in the identical column can *never* enter a solution. Hence that column can be eliminated entirely from the array.

In general, then, when two or more columns in an array are identical, element for element, the column with the most algebraically maximum objective number is retained. The remaining identical column(s) is (are) entirely deleted from the array. The removal of redundant columns in no way affects the problem or its solution(s). It does, however, reduce some of the calculations required in successive iterations. This can, in some instances, reduce the problem to where the optimum solution is obvious.

Algebraic Substitution. Algebraic substitution also offers a convenient means of reducing the size of a formulation in certain situations. For example, consider a problem somewhat similar to a previous problem. Maximize:

$$11x + 4y$$

subject to

$$7x + 6y \leq 84 \qquad (1)$$

$$4x + 2y \leq 32 \qquad (2)$$

$$x \geq 2 \qquad (3)$$

$$y \geq 3 \qquad (4)$$

where relationships 1 and 2 represent equipment producing capacity limitations, and relationships 3 and 4 can be considered as firm customer orders or commitments.

The above problem can be set up for the simplex method and put into a matrix array rather easily. The two restrictions 1 and 2 merely require the addition of a slack variable. The two requirements 3 and 4 must have a slack variable subtracted and then an artificial variable added. The system would then be: Maximize,

$$11x + 4y + 0 \cdot W_1 + 0 \cdot W_2 + 0 \cdot W_3 + 0 \cdot W_4 - MU_1 - MU_2$$

subject to

$$7x + 6y + W_1 = 84 \tag{1}$$
$$4x + 2y + W_2 = 32 \tag{2}$$
$$x - W_3 + U_1 = 2 \tag{3}$$
$$y - W_4 + U_2 = 3 \tag{4}$$

The problem is then represented by a system of four equations combining eight unknowns or a 4 × 8 simplex matrix array as indicated in Figure 72.

			11	4	0	0	0	0	−M	−M
			x	y	W_3	W_4	W_1	W_2	U_1	U_2
0	W_1	84	7	6	0	0	1	0	0	0
0	W_2	32	4	2	0	0	0	1	0	0
−M	U_1	2	1	0	−1	0	0	0	1	0
−M	U_2	3	0	1	0	−1	0	0	0	1

Fig. 72. Initial Simplex Matrix before Simplification

This problem can be simplified by algebraic substitution, thereby materially reducing the matrix dimensions and the amount of calculation. If, in the original system, maximize

$$11x + 4y$$

subject to

$$7x + 6y \leq 84$$
$$4x + 2y \leq 32$$
$$x \geq 2$$
$$y \geq 3$$

we let

$$x' = x - 2$$
$$y' = y - 3$$

then, from relationships 3 and 4, since

$$x - 2 \geq 0$$
$$y - 3 \geq 0$$

it follows that

$$x' \geq 0$$
$$y' \geq 0$$

which need not be explicitly written since it is implicit in the simplex method. We then substitute.

$$x' + 2 = x$$
$$y' + 3 = y$$

and the system becomes: Maximize

$$11(x' + 2) + 4(y' + 3)$$

or

$$11x' + 4y' + 34$$

subject to

$$7(x' + 2) + 6(y' + 3) \leq 84$$
$$7x' + 6y' \leq 52 \qquad (1')$$

$$4(x' + 2) + 2(y' + 3) \leq 32$$
$$4x' + 2y' \leq 18 \qquad (2')$$

$$(x' + 2) \geq 2$$
$$x' \geq 0 \qquad (3')$$

$$(y' + 3) \geq 3$$
$$y' \geq 0 \qquad (4')$$

Since the relationships 3′ and 4′ are implicitly met in the simplex method, these need not be explicitly written. Hence the problem is now expressed effectively in two restrictions, and the initial simplex matrix is as shown in Figure 73.

		−34	11	4	0	0
			x'	y'	W_1	W_2
0	W_1	52	7	6	1	0
0	W_2	18	4	2	0	1

Fig. 73. Initial Simplex Matrix after Simplification

It is rather obvious that a considerable degree of work has been saved by the algebraic substitution. In this case, the problem matrix is one quarter of its former size. Note that the number in the constant column and objective row is not zero as it always has been up to now. In situations where algebraic substitution has been employed, the objective function no longer represents the true objective function of the problem as originally stated. This modified objective function, when used with the simplex method, will not yield the true optimum value if the constant part of the function is not included as shown in the matrix (Fig. 73). If we consider the

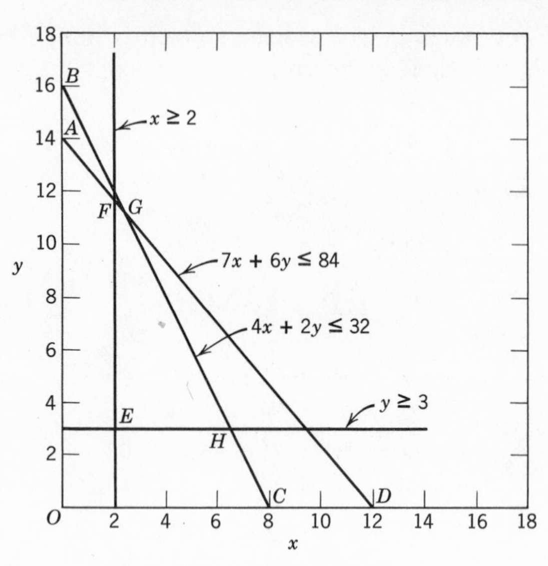

Fig. 74. Problem Graph

geometric analysis of this problem, this point can be more readily seen.

In Figure 74, all four of the problem relationships are shown. The four relationships enclose an area *EFGH* as the area of possible solutions to the system. Essentially what the algebraic substitution accomplished was to move the origin from O to E so that the problem in variables x' and y' appears graphically as in Figure 75.

In the graph of the simplified problem (Fig. 75), we can see how the two requirements are now the ordinate and abscissa of the new variables graph. Area *EFGH* is the area of possible solutions.

In the objective function, if the -34 is dropped in constructing the matrix array, then the optimum value for the objective function will apply to the variables x' and y'. If, however, the -34 is retained (as in Fig. 73), then the optimum value of the objective function will apply to the real variables x and y, and the simplex calculations will yield the optimum value of the real objective function directly.

Many possible substitutions may be employed, depending on the problem at hand. Almost any kind of substitution is valid as long as no possibility exists for a negative value of a real problem variable. For example, if we attempt a substitution where

$$x \leq 10$$

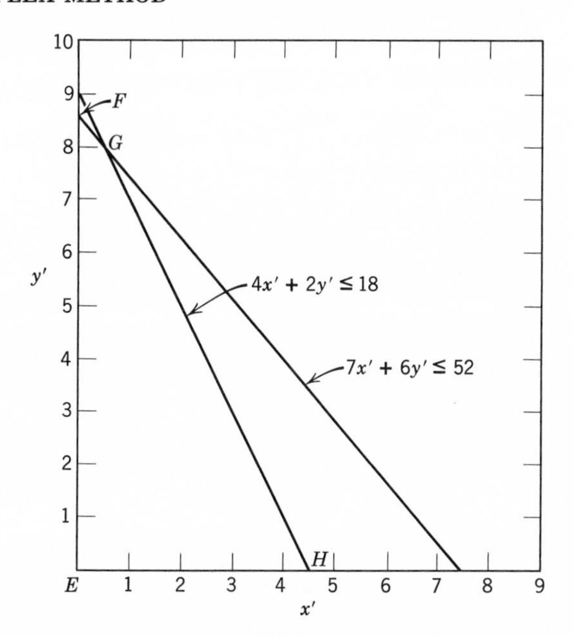

Fig. 75. Simplified Problem Graph

then

$$x - 10 \leq 0$$

We can multiply both sides of the relationship by -1 and reverse the inequality sign so that

$$-x + 10 \geq 0$$

If we let

$$x' = -x + 10 \geq 0$$

and proceed with this substitution, the resulting formulation will not be valid. The above substitution is no good in that, if x' should attain a value larger than 10, the real problem variable x will be negative. For example, if

$$x' = 15$$

then

$$x' = -x + 10$$
$$x = 10 - 15$$
$$x = -5$$

which means that the variable x is consumed rather than created, and violates the basic requisite that all variables be greater than or equal to zero. The above substitution could be used if the restriction

$$x' \leq 10$$

is included in the formulation. This, however, defeats the simplification purpose of substitution, since the problem remains the same size as before the substitution.

In many problem formulations, particularly if the problem is to be solved by hand, the time is well spent in investigating simplification possibilities. Algebraic simplification is very evident in problem formulations. Redundant columns are easily recognized and eliminated. However, it is generally more difficult to spot redundant relationships in a system, in that they are not always so obvious as in the preceding example.

DISTRIBUTION-TYPE PROBLEMS

Distribution-type problems like those presented in the preceding chapter can be solved with the simplex method. Actually it is foolish even to consider using the simplex method to solve distribution problems, owing to the simplicity of the distribution methods. However, it is worth while to look at the characteristics of distribution problems in the simplex set-up because occasionally one may encounter a problem that might be simplified into a distribution-problem form and solved much more easily.

Consider the distribution problem from the preceding chapter:

Supply	Units	Demand	Units
Flint	150	Chicago	90
Janesville	40	Cleveland	70
St. Louis	80	Dayton	50
		Minneapolis	60
	270		270

Shipping costs per unit:

From \ To	Chicago	Cleveland	Dayton	Minneapolis
Flint	$27.00	$23.00	$31.00	$69.00
Janesville	10.00	45.00	40.00	32.00
St. Louis	30.00	54.00	35.00	57.00

This problem can be formulated as follows: Let

x_{ij} = number of units shipped from source i to destination j
c_{ij} = shipping cost per unit from source i to destination j
S_i = number of units of supply at source i
D_j = number of units of demand at destination j
i = (1, 2, 3) the supply points
j = (1, 2, 3, 4) the customers or shipping destinations

then the supply can be expressed as

$$x_{11} + x_{12} + x_{13} + x_{14} = S_1 = 150 \quad (1)$$
$$x_{21} + x_{22} + x_{23} + x_{24} = S_2 = 40 \quad (2)$$
$$x_{31} + x_{32} + x_{33} + x_{34} = S_3 = 80 \quad (3)$$

and the demand

$$x_{11} + x_{21} + x_{31} = D_1 = 90 \quad (4)$$
$$x_{12} + x_{22} + x_{32} = D_2 = 70 \quad (5)$$
$$x_{13} + x_{23} + x_{33} = D_3 = 50 \quad (6)$$
$$x_{14} + x_{24} + x_{34} = D_4 = 60 \quad (7)$$

and the objective function is

$$27x_{11} + 23x_{12} + 31x_{13} + \cdots + 35x_{33} + 57x_{34} = \text{minimum}$$

Hence the 3 $\times$ 4 distribution problem from the preceding chapter is expressed in the above seven equations. The equations can be readied for the simplex method by the addition of artificial variables. The objective function must be maximizing rather than minimizing. Therefore, the problem must appear as: Maximize

$$-27x_{11} - 23x_{12} - 31x_{13} - \cdots - 35x_{33} - 57x_{34} - MU_1 - \cdots - MU_7$$

subject to

$$x_{11} + x_{12} + x_{13} + x_{14} + U_1 = 150 \quad (1)$$
$$x_{21} + x_{22} + x_{23} + x_{24} + U_2 = 40 \quad (2)$$
$$x_{31} + x_{32} + x_{33} + x_{34} + U_3 = 80 \quad (3)$$
$$x_{11} + x_{21} + x_{31} + U_4 = 90 \quad (4)$$
$$x_{12} + x_{22} + x_{32} + U_5 = 70 \quad (5)$$
$$x_{13} + x_{23} + x_{33} + U_6 = 50 \quad (6)$$
$$x_{14} + x_{24} + x_{34} + U_7 = 60 \quad (7)$$

This formulation would then appear as shown in Figure 76.

Two important characteristics can be noted in this distribution problem. All the coefficients of the variables are unity, and they fall into a rather orderly pattern (a row of one's with a stair-step

			-27	-23	-31	-69	-10	-45	-40	-32	-30	-54	-35	-57	$-M$	$-M$	$-M$	$-M$	$-M$	$-M$	$-M$
			x_{11}	x_{12}	x_{13}	x_{14}	x_{21}	x_{22}	x_{23}	x_{24}	x_{31}	x_{32}	x_{33}	x_{34}	U_1	U_2	U_3	U_4	U_5	U_6	U_7
$-M$	U_1	150	1	1	1	1									1						
$-M$	U_2	40					1	1	1	1						1					
$-M$	U_3	80									1	1	1	1			1				
$-M$	U_4	90	1				1				1							1			
$-M$	U_5	70		1				1				1							1		
$-M$	U_6	50			1				1				1							1	
$-M$	U_7	60				1				1				1							1

Fig. 76. Distribution Problem in the Simplex Set-up

pattern of one's) in the simplex matrix. This is characteristic of all distribution-type problems. If a problem is formulated and appears in the matrix array with this type of pattern, then the problem is a distribution-type problem and can be much more easily solved with the distribution methods previously outlined. An additional advantage is derived in using the distribution methods in that one does not usually have to deal with as many artificial variables and their $-M$ costs.

The characteristic arrangement of numbers in the simplex matrix array can be used as the basis for some approximation solutions. In some problems it may be possible to modify the matrix arrangement and to approximate unity numbers so that the problem can be solved more quickly and easily as a distribution problem. Consider a simplex matrix (body of the array only) as shown in Figure 77.

	3	−6	4	2	5	3	8	6	−2	12
	x_1	x_2	x_3	x_4	x_5	x_6	x_7	x_8	x_9	x_{10}
200	9	11	10	8	12					
60						1	1.3	1.1	0.85	0.90
12	2					1				
33		2					1			
15			2					1		
14				2					1	
28					2					1

Fig. 77. A Problem Formulation Exhibiting the Distribution-Problem Pattern

This particular array has the pattern of a distribution problem, but it lacks unit numbers in the array. However, the unit number pattern can be effectively approximated if we divide the first five columns by two (element by element). Then, if the first row is divided by 5 and the numbers are rounded off to unity, and if the numbers of the second row are rounded off to unity, the distribution pattern exists (Fig. 78).

	1.5	−3	2	1	2.5	3	8	6	−2	12
	x'_1	x'_2	x'_3	x'_4	x'_5	x_6	x_7	x_8	x_9	x_{10}
40	1	1	1	1	1					
60						1	1	1	1	1
12	1					1				
33		1					1			
15			1					1		
14				1					1	
28					1					1

Fig. 78. A Problem Formulation with Distribution Pattern Approximated

These manipulations are completely legitimate because in matrix algebra one can do any of the following without changing the value of the matrix:

1. Any row(s) or any column(s) may be interchanged in position in the array.
2. Any row(s) or any column(s) may be multiplied element by element by any quantity.

The problem (Fig. 78) has the exact distribution form. Note that the first five columns are now indicated as x primes (x'_1, x'_2, $\cdots$, x'_5) because they are not now exactly the same variables as before. Note also how the numbers in the first two rows have been rounded off to unity. This means that the formulation as it now stands is an approximation to the exact formulation (Fig. 77). However, the problem can now be represented as a 3×5 distribution problem (Fig. 79), which can be rather easily solved.

From \ To	*f*	*g*	*h*	*i*	*j*	Supply
a	1.5	−3	2	1	2.5	40
b	3	8	6	−2	12	60
Dummy	0	0	0	0	0	2
Demand	12	33	15	14	28	102

Fig. 79. Distribution Matrix Approximation of Problem from Fig. 77

It must be kept in mind that the solution to the distribution form of the problem (Fig. 79) is really an approximation. That solution may have to be slightly altered in order to obtain a practical solution to the original problem. However, it is evident that considerable time and effort can be saved in solving the problem in this manner. The approximate solution may be within 10 per cent (or less) of the very best solution and can therefore be more truly optimum when the cost of the solution is considered in any comparison. This and other approximation methods are more fully expanded later in the book.

THE DUAL PROBLEM

For most mathematical programming problems it is possible to formulate the problem in two ways. These two formulations are generally referred to as the primal and dual problems.[26] An example of the primal and dual problems can be shown via the manufacturing problem presented earlier in this chapter.

The manufacturing problem presented earlier (to illustrate the basic simplex method) was represented by the formulation: Maximize

$$11x + 4y$$

subject to

$$7x + 6y \leq 84$$
$$4x + 2y \leq 32$$

[26] Charnes, Cooper, and Henderson, *op. cit.*, pp. 31–36.

The above system appears in tabular form

	11	4
	x	y
$84 \geq$	7	6
$32 \geq$	4	2

It can be seen that the formulation was prepared horizontally with the preceding number array. Suppose now that we assign new variables (z_1 and z_2) to the first and second rows, respectively. Then it would be possible to prepare a formulation vertically. The original formulation of the problem will be referred to as the primal problem. The matrix appears as follows:

		11	4
		x	y
z_1	$84 \geq$	7	6
z_2	$32 \geq$	4	2

If we cross out the old variables x and y, then the formulation of the dual problem may result as follows. Minimize

$$84z_1 + 32z_2$$

subject to

$$7z_1 + 4z_2 \geq 11$$
$$6z_1 + 2z_2 \geq 4$$

or

	-84	-32
	z_1	z_2
$11 \leq$	7	4
$4 \leq$	6	2

Note that the objective (maximization or minimization) of the dual problem is the reverse of the primal problem. Note also that the constant column of the primal problem becomes the objective function of the dual. Similarly, the objective function of the primal is the constant column of the dual problem. It can be seen also that the inequality signs are reversed in the dual problem. These changes and comparisons are completely general and apply equally well to any problem formulation. Figure 80 shows the successive iterations of the simplex solution to the dual for this particular problem.

By this time the diligent reader will probably wonder about the

			-84	-32	0	0	$-M$	$-M$		
			z_1	z_2	W'_1	W'_2	U_1	U_2		ck
$-M$	U_1	11	7	4	-1	0	1	0		22
$-M$	U_2	4	6	2	0	-1	0	1		12
		$-15M$	$-13M +84$	$-6M +32$	M	M	0	0		$-32M +116$
$-M$	U_1	$19/3$	0	$5/3$	-1	$7/6$	1	$-7/6$		8
-84	z_1	$2/3$	1	$1/3$	0	$-1/6$	0	$1/6$		2
		$-\frac{19M}{3} -56$	0	$-\frac{5M}{3} +4$	M	$-\frac{7M}{6} +14$	0	$\frac{13M}{6} -14$		$-6M -52$
$-M$	U_1	3	-5	0	-1	2	1	-2		-2
-32	z_2	2	3	1	0	$-1/2$	0	$1/2$		6
		$-3M -64$	$+5M -12$	0	M	$-2M +16$	0	$3M -16$		$4M -76$
0	W'_2	$3/2$	$-5/2$	0	$-1/2$	1	$1/2$	-1		-1
-32	z_2	$1\frac{1}{4}$	$7/4$	1	$-1/4$	0	$1/4$	0		$1\frac{1}{2}$
		-88	28	0	8	0	$M -8$	M		$2M -60$

Fig. 80. Simplex Solution to the Dual of the Manufacturing Problem

practical value of the dual problem and what definition can be attached to the variables in the dual. In the particular problem shown, it is very evident that the dual presents considerably more work to solve than the primal problem (a 2×6 matrix solved in three iterations for the dual versus a 2×4 matrix solved in one iteration for the primal). However, in other problem situations the reverse may be true; hence the dual would then be easier to solve.

The variables in the dual formulation (z_1 and z_2) do have a very realistic interpretation. These variables actually represent the marginal profit (or costs, if it were the case) for the two manufacturing processes. To clarify this point let us look at the solutions (optimum matrices) to both the primal and dual problems.

Primal Solution

			11	4	W_1	W_2
			x	y	W_1	W_2
0	W_1	28	0	$\frac{5}{2}$	1	$-\frac{7}{4}$
11	x	8	1	$\frac{1}{2}$	0	$\frac{1}{4}$
		88	0	$\frac{3}{2}$	0	$1\frac{1}{4}$

Dual Solution

			-84	-32	0	0	$-M$	$-M$
			z_1	z_2	W'_1	W'_2	U_1	U_2
0	W'_2	$\frac{3}{2}$	$-\frac{5}{2}$	0	$-\frac{1}{2}$	1	$\frac{1}{2}$	-1
-32	z_2	$1\frac{1}{4}$	$\frac{7}{4}$	1	$-\frac{1}{4}$	0	$\frac{1}{4}$	0
		-88	28	0	8	0	$M-8$	M

Fig. 81. Optimum Solution Matrices for Both the Primal and Dual of a Problem

In the analysis and interpretation of the optimum solution matrix for the primal problem, we established an interpretation for all the numbers in the constant column and index row. The interpretation is:

Constant column numbers—represent the value of the variables in the solution.

Index row numbers

Under the body of the matrix—represent the amount of algebraic decrease in the objective function if one unit of that variable were introduced into the solution.

Under the identity—represent the opportunity profit or potential algebraic increase in the objective function if one more of that variable were available in the initial solution.

In terms of economics, the numbers in the index row actually represent the marginal profit (or cost) of the variables in the respective columns. We can note from the solution to the primal problem the marginal profit (or cost) for variables y and W_2.

$$\text{Marginal profit for } y = \tfrac{3}{2}$$
$$\text{Marginal profit for } W_2 = 1\tfrac{1}{4}$$

We can then see that these two marginal values coincide with the values of W'_2 and z_2 in the dual solution. Therefore, the variables in the dual represent the marginal profit or cost for the variables of zero value in the optimum solution to the primal problem. A similar analysis holds true for the index row numbers of the dual solution.

Solution, then, of the primal also solves the dual or vice versa. One can see from Figure 81, if one solution (either the primal or dual) is obtained, that the entire matrix array for the other solution can be rather easily constructed. This fact, then, permits one to formulate and solve either the primal or dual problem, whichever is the easier. In general, a formulation with fewer rows will require fewer iterations.[27] In examples such as the one preceding, where both primal and dual formulations have the same number of rows, the formulation with fewer columns will generally require less work.

The general form of the dual programming problem illustrates the comparison between primal and dual formulations. The general form of the primal is to maximize a function z where

$$z = cx$$

subject to

$$Ax \leq b$$
$$x \geq 0$$

where z = the maximizing objective function
c = the objective coefficients of the variables
x = the variables of the problem
A = the matrix array—the coefficients of the variables in the various restrictions of the problem
b = the numbers of the constant column

The dual formulation for this primal is to minimize a function g where

$$g = bw$$

subject to

$$wA' \geq c$$
$$w \geq 0$$

where w = the variables of the dual corresponding to the marginal cost or profit of the variables of the primal
A' = the transpose matrix array of the primal

The remaining definitions for the symbols are the same as for the primal.

A problem formulation must be put in either of the above forms

---

[27] Charnes, Cooper, and Henderson, *op. cit.*, p. 33.

in order to formulate the dual. The dual formulation can be accomplished for a system that contains equations; however, this is beyond the scope of this textbook.

Knowledge of the dual formulation and its interpretation can be of considerable value in many larger problems by permitting a solution to be obtained via whichever formulation is more computationally convenient. Then, too, the real problem may actually require only the marginal costs or profits, or the solution to the dual rather than primal formulation. It has been indicated[28] that the dual could be used to establish these marginal costs or profits or "shadow prices," and thereby provide management with a guide to operating alternatives at various levels of operation.

MODIFIED SIMPLEX METHOD[29]

Up to this point the discussion has centered about the basic simplex method, which can be successfully used to solve all types of linear programming problems. However, as one encounters typical problems, the question of computational efficiency arises, particularly in problems involving artificial variables, whether the problems are solved by hand or with automatic calculating machines. The modified simplex method affords a convenient means of dealing with the high-cost factors ($-M$) associated with artificial variables. In solving these matrices by hand, the $-M$ cost factors make the calculations in the index row very tedious and cumbersome. Then, too, an artificial variable may remain in the successive solutions until one of the last iterations, causing more work in every iteration.

In using automatic calculating equipment another difficulty arises. The $-M$ must be assigned some numerical value many times larger than the other coefficients in the objective function. This means that the calculating equipment must be capable of handling widely differing numerical values. Then, too, if one does not choose the numerical value for $-M$ rather judiciously, it is possible that one or more artificial variables will remain in the optimum solution, yielding an incorrect solution to the problem.

The modified simplex method or two-phase simplex method has

[28] *Ibid.* See also Koopmans, *op. cit.*

[29] Also known as the "two-phase method."

been developed along two lines; hand and automatic computation. One group from the Rand Corporation, notably G. B. Dantzig and W. Orchard-Hays,[30] and one group from International Business Machines Corporation, notably Kurt Eiseman,[31] have developed the modified simplex method from the standpoint of calculating efficiency with high-speed computing equipment. A very suitable extension of the method, primarily for hand calculation, has been presented by H. M. Wagner.[32] The essence of the hand-calculation method will be presented here.

In general, the modified simplex method can be applied to problems involving artificial variables and requires two phases or sets of calculations.

Phase I involves solving the problem with the usual simplex method but with a modified objective function. The objective function established is one that tends to minimize the artificial variables or it would appear: Maximize

$$0 \cdot x_1 + 0 \cdot x_2 + \cdots + 0 \cdot W_1 + 0 \cdot W_2 - \cdots - U_1 - U_2 - \cdots$$

where x_1, x_2, x_i = real variables
W_1, W_2, W_i = slack variables
U_1, U_2, U_i = artificial variables

In phase I, the system remains unchanged; only the objective function is modified as indicated above.

Phase II takes place after phase I is complete and involves replacing the modified objective function of phase I with the real objective function of the problem, revising the index row values, and continuing with the basic simplex calculations until an optimum has been obtained. Phase II will take either of two courses, depending on the problem at hand.

In the first case, where phase I eliminates all the artificial variables, then phase II can proceed straight forward as indicated above. In the second case, phase I has not eliminated all the artificial variables, and some remain in the solution stub with a zero

---

[30] See Bibliography for a listing of the works of these two authors in this area.

[31] K. Eiseman, "Linear Programming," *Quarterly of Applied Mathematics,* V. XIII, No. 3, October 1955, pp. 209–323. See also K. Eiseman, "Linear Programming—Recursive Generation of Vectors for the Modified Simplex Method," IBM (mimeographed), New York, 1956.

[32] H. M. Wagner, "A Two Phase Method for the Simplex Tableau," *Journal of Operations Research Society of America,* V. 4, No. 4, August 1956, pp. 443–447.

value.[33] Here it is required that the index row be brought into the array, and the array increased by another row and column, in order to continue with phase II. This will be further developed after a sample problem is used to illustrate the first case of the modified simplex method.

Consider the system developed previously (Fig. 80) as representing a problem formulation[34] where we wish to: Maximize

$$-84z_1 - 32z_2$$

subject to

$$7z_1 + 4z_2 \geq 11$$
$$6z_1 + 2z_2 \geq 4$$

Figure 80 shows the successive iterations in solving this problem. Here is an example where one artificial variable remains until the last iteration, causing manipulation of many complex index row numbers involving the $-M$ cost factor. If we wished to apply the modified simplex method to solving this problem, the objective function must be temporarily modified to: Maximize

$$-U_1 - U_2$$

where the complete system (including necessary slack and artificial variables) is

$$7z_1 + 4z_2 - W'_1 + U_1 = 11$$
$$6z_1 + 2z_2 - W'_2 + U_2 = 4$$

Figure 82 shows the phase I calculation of the modified simplex method for this problem. Note that phase I requires the same number of iterations (three iterations) as in the solution to the problem with the basic simplex method (Fig. 80). It can be easily seen that the numbers in the index rows are considerably simpler and require less time and effort to calculate.

At the completion of phase I, since no artificial variables remain in the solution stub, phase II can proceed by merely inserting the

---

[33] It can be verified that, for an optimum to exist, the artificial variables remaining in the stub must have a zero value. If one or more artificial variables have a value > 0, and all index row values are ≥ 0, then no optimum solution exists for the problem, and either the formulation is in error, or the problem has no feasible solution. In dealing with problems in the real world, more than likely the former will be true. See Charnes, Cooper, and Henderson, *op. cit.*, p. 17.

[34] Forget for the moment that this problem has a rather easily solved dual. This problem will permit rather easy comprehension of the modified simplex method.

			0	0	0	0	−1	−1	
			z_1	z_2	W'_1	W'_2	U_1	U_2	ck
−1	U_1	11	7	4	−1	0	1	0	22
−1	U_2	4	6	2	0	−1	0	1	12
		−15	−13	−6	1	1	0	0	−32
−1	U_1	19/3	0	5/3	−1	7/6	1	−7/6	8
0	z_1	2/3	1	1/3	0	−1/6	0	1/6	2
		−19/3	0	−5/3	1	−7/6	0	13/6	−6
−1	U_1	3	−5	0	−1	2	1	−2	−2
0	z_2	2	3	1	0	−1/2	0	1/2	6
		−3	5	0	1	−2	0	3	4
0	W'_2	3/2	−5/2	0	−1/2	1	1/2	−1	−1
0	z_2	11/4	7/4	1	−1/4	0	1/4	0	11/2
		0	0	0	0	0	1	1	2

Fig. 82. Phase I Modified—Simplex Method

correct objective function and calculating the proper index row. No further work will be required in phase II because in this problem the optimum was obtained by phase I.

Occasionally problems will require an iteration or so in phase II.

			−84	−32	0	0	−M	−M	
			z_1	z_2	W'_1	W'_2	U_1	U_2	ck
0	W'_2	3/2	−5/2	0	−1/2	1	1/2	−1	−1
−32	z_2	11/4	7/4	1	−1/4	0	1/4	0	11/2
		−88	28	0	8	0	M −8	M	2M −60

Fig. 83. Phase II Modified Simplex Method—Optimum Solution Obtained by Part I

Note: The −M's were re-established for the artificial variables. The −M's could have been replaced by zeros as long as the artificial variables are not permitted, regardless of index number, to re-enter the stub in any successive iteration.

Usually the number of iterations with the modified simplex method will be of the same order as in the basic simplex method. The advantage in the modified simplex method as shown in the above example is in elimination of the artificial variables and their $-M$ cost coefficients in a very efficient manner.

Sometimes phase I will not eliminate all of the artificial variables from the solution stub. When several remain in the solution stub with a zero value,[35] then phase II must be handled slightly differently. Before phase II can begin, it is necessary to retain the index row of the last iteration of phase I by bringing it into the matrix array as an additional row. This also requires that a new variable (we will use Q here) be assigned for that new row, and a column with this variable created at the right-hand end of the array (see Fig. 84). The solution may then be attained by straightforward application of the simplex method after the original objective function is reinstated and the new index row calculated. It is recom-

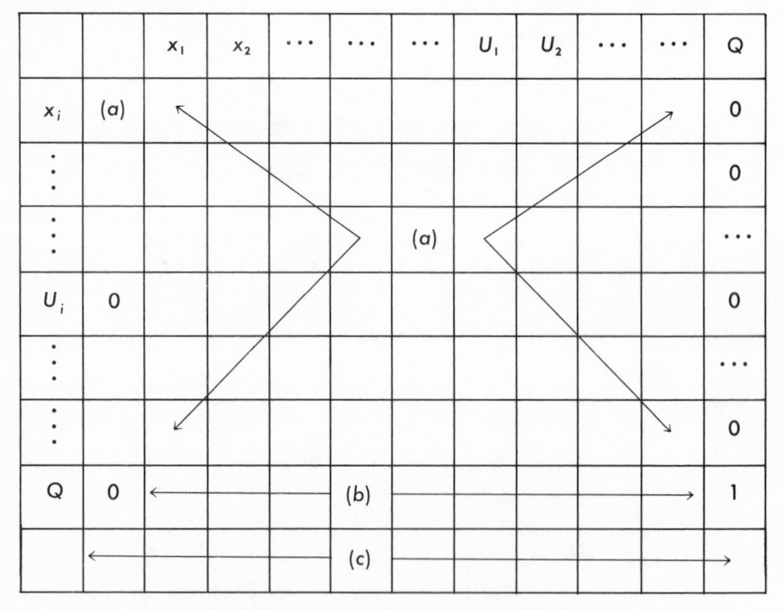

Fig. 84. Matrix Organization for Phase II—Modified Simplex Method

a. The matrix array as obtained in phase I
b. The index row from phase I
c. The index row for phase II

[35] See comment contained in footnote 33.

mended that zero's be assigned to the artificial variables instead of the original $-M$'s.

The variable Q in phase II must never be considered as the key row in any subsequent iterations. The variable Q is assigned a zero cost in the objective row; hence the new row will not affect the phase II index row values. This new row in the matrix is equivalent to an additional redundant equation which assures that all the artificial variables remaining in the stub in successive iterations will be zero. This, thereby, permits the computations to continue with a zero cost rather than the $-M$'s attached to the artificial variables.

The modified simplex method, while it does not change the basic simplex method, does offer an efficient means of handling problems with many artificial variables. The relative ease in computing with -1 costs (phase I) and zero costs (phase II) for the artificial variables is rather evident in the previous example. Though one may not necessarily encounter many problems of this type, the modified simplex method is a useful and worth-while extension of the basic simplex method.

SUMMARY

The simplex method has been presented in an understandable step-by-step manner. The problems and examples, though they are not actual problems in the real world, were chosen as illustrative examples. Subsequent chapters will follow the step-by-step development and solution of typical business and industrial problems.

It may be well to consider here in summary the major requirements of a linear programming problem. They are:

1. There must be a number of choices, alternatives or ways of taking action.

2. There must be a rate of efficiency difference between the alternatives.

3. There must be an interrelationship of the variables in significant expressions (the system of relationships).

4. There must be a set of restrictions, or upper limits, or that which must not be exceeded. (This may be implicit in a problem.)

5. There must be a set of requirements, or lower limits, or that which must at least be accomplished. (This is very often implicit in the formulation.)

6. There must be an objective or goal to strive to attain (minimum costs, maximum profits, etc.).

7. There must be common units of measure for the variables.

The above are necessary for a linear programming problem, but they are not necessarily sufficient in themselves for all problems.

One can see, from the above, that linear programming has one very stringent limitation, in that the variables must be combined in linear expressions. Although many types of problems fit within this limitation, there are many more that do not. Considering the relative newness of the entire field of mathematical programming, it seems feasible that further research should be able, in time, to circumvent this and other limitations. Some work has been done to date in nonlinear and quadratic programming[36] for other classes of problems.

The simplex method is usually used to solve systems of linear inequalities, but it compares very favorably with the usual elimination methods in solving systems of linear equations. In fact, the modified simplex method would seem to offer an even better approach to solving these types of problems, either by hand or with computing equipment.

The simplex method and its various short-cuts, extensions, and simplifications are not really too difficult. In fact, the method can be successfully taught to individuals who have had little more than high school freshman algebra. This, by no means, implies that anyone can tackle mathematical programming problems. Considerable knowledge and skill are required to recognize a problem and to formulate the problem properly. When the problem is solved, usually more skill is required again in analyzing the solution and its alternatives, and in presenting them to management in terms that they will understand as possible courses of action. Here is where the talent must be developed, in recognizing a problem, in preparing the formulation, and in analyzing the final solution(s). Subsequent chapters will consider various examples, some hypothetical, some from actual situations in industry, to illustrate types of problems and their formulation and solution via mathematical programming.

---

[36] L. E. Saline, "Quadratic Programming of Interdependent Activities for Optimum Performance," ASME paper No. 54-A-58, 1954, 21 pp.

4. Approximation Methods

Many problems may be suitably solved by an appropriate approximation. Very often an approximation to the optimum may be more useful and economical than the absolute optimum solution. There are, in general, four problem situations where approximation methods can be employed. These are:

1. When the approximate solution presents sufficient information for decisions—this type of problem solving is directed at providing better information for management decisions. Often an approximate solution can provide that information without the more formal mathematical solution.

2. When the mathematical formulation is too large for computation—without data-processing equipment, this size limitation can be very easily reached. Size is often a limiting factor, even with suitable calculating equipment. In these cases, then, the approximate solution is the only solution obtainable.

3. When the additional return from the optimum solution is less than the additional effort or cost required—often an approximate solution is so close to the mathematically optimum that the additional cost of the optimum solution is not justifiable. Here, when one considers the broader economic comparison, the approximate solution is more truly optimum than the mathematically optimum solution.

4. When the data in the formulation are estimated—often one must estimate data in constructing a formulation. Here, then, the mathematically optimum solution is very questionable. Usually an approximation to the optimum will present a suitable solution.

Several approximation methods are considered here. They run the gamut from little more than a formalized inspection routine to rather involved mathematical methods. Not all the approximations discussed here have proper names, and by no means do these represent all the possible approximation methods. Often an approximation method is tailored to the particular problem at hand; hence they may be unlimited in number and variety. The index method, nora method, approximation to multidimensional distribution problems, and a means of bounding the optimum value of the objective function will be discussed.

THE INDEX METHOD

The index method is a relatively simple approximation method for solving product allocation problems—more specifically in determining what process should produce what job(s) so that the least total time (or money) is spent in manufacturing. This method is dependent, to a large extent, upon a degree of judgment on the part of the person solving the problem. The method can best be seen via a small problem.

A Problem. An organization must schedule ten orders on four machines. They are interested in improving upon the present means of scheduling and machine assignment. The orders and the time requirements on the various machines are as shown in Figure 85.

Often the producing alternatives are not recognized, and rarely is the information organized as in Figure 85. The person assigning this work to the machines might make the assignments as the orders are received: assigning orders to the best machine until it is fully loaded, then to the second best machine, etc. This type of assignment plan would result, in the problem at hand, in assignments as shown in Table 7.

The assignments are such that they can be accomplished in the available machine time. However, it may be possible by slightly different assignments to accomplish all the work in less total time. If this is possible, then the manufacturing capacity of the machines

Order No.	Time Required per Order, hours Machines			
	A	B	C	D
1	10	12	18	25
2	5	6	12	18
3	8	8	10	15
4	12	14	14	20
5	20	25	27	35
6	15	19	23	30
7	14	14	16	20
8	17	19	25	27
9	8	10	16	30
10	9	12	18	25
Total Available Time	40	40	40	120

Fig. 85. Time Required per Order on the Various Machines

Note: The time values include necessary set-up and tear-down.

will be increased, thereby allowing more work to be accomplished in the same time.

One means of improving the assignments is by inspecting the net effect upon total time requirements of trading orders from one machine to another. With practice, this can become a reasonably efficient means of obtaining better machine-load assignments. However, as with most inspection methods, this becomes increasingly complex as the number of orders and number of machines increases. A regular machine-shop schedule with at least 10 to 20 machines and one hundred or more orders would present an almost unsolvable problem by most means of inspection.

Table 7

Order No.	Assigned to Machine	Time Required, hours
1	A	10
2	A	5
3	A	8
4	A	12
5	B	25
6	C	23
7	B	14
8	D	27
9	C	16
10	D	25
	Total Time Required	155 hours

In analyzing work-assignment problems, like the one shown in Figure 85, the relationship between the time values for an order on the various machines must be considered. This relationship leads to the development of the index method for machine assignment. The index method utilizes the same problem organization as in Figure 85 with the addition of index numbers. Every order has an index number for every alternative machine (the index number is one for the best machine: i.e., the one with the lowest manufacturing time). The index number is the quotient of the actual machine time divided by the very best machine time.

$$\text{Index number} = \frac{\text{actual machine time}}{\text{best machine time}}$$

For example, the index numbers for order 1 are:

Machine A = (no index number since this is the best machine)

$$\text{Machine } B = \frac{12 \text{ (actual time)}}{10 \text{ (best time)}} = 1.2$$

$$\text{Machine } C = \frac{18}{10} = 1.8$$

$$\text{Machine } D = \frac{25}{10} = 2.5$$

Actually the index numbers indicate the time relationship between an alternative machine and the best machine (i.e., machine B requires 1.2 times as much time as machine A for order 1). Index numbers are rather easily determined for the remaining orders and are as shown in Figure 86. Note that the index numbers are in parenthesis so as not to confuse them with the machine time per order.

The index method develops the machine assignments in the following steps:

1. Assume that all work is assigned to the very best machine. This then overloads the very best machine.

2. Find the order with the smallest index number in the columns for the alternative machines (*B*, *C*, and *D* in this case).

3. Remove that order from the very best machine, and assign it to where the index number is the smallest. Assign the order to the lowest-order alternative machine if two or more have the same index number.

4. Check the remaining time requirements for the very best machine.

	Hours per Order and Index Number Machines			
Order	A	B	C	D
1	10	12 (1.2)	18 (1.8)	25 (2.5)
2	5	6 (1.2)	12 (2.4)	18 (3.6)
3	8	8 (1.0)	10 (1.25)	15 (1.88)
4	12	14 (1.17)	14 (1.17)	20 (1.67)
5	20	25 (1.25)	27 (1.35)	35 (1.75)
6	15	19 (1.26)	23 (1.53)	30 (2.0)
7	14	14 (1.0)	16 (1.14)	20 (1.43)
8	17	19 (1.12)	25 (1.47)	27 (1.59)
9	8	10 (1.25)	16 (2.0)	30 (3.75)
10	9	12 (1.34)	18 (2.0)	25 (2.78)
Total Available Time	40	40	40	120

Fig. 86. Machine-Assignment Problem—Index Numbers Shown

5. Continue steps 1 through 4 until the work load on the best machine is less than or equal to the available time. In repeating step 2, omit from consideration the index numbers for the orders previously removed from the best machine. Assignments must be made within the available time on each machine.

The index method in the problem at hand will assign orders 3 and 7 to machine *B,* since these orders each have an index number of 1.0 on machine *B.* Then order 8 is assigned to *B* since the index number is 1.12. This assignment, however, is not valid because orders 3, 7, and 8 require 41 hours of machine time on *B,* and only 40 hours are available. The next lowest index number is 1.14 for order 7 on machine *C.* However, order 7 has already been assigned and hence cannot be considered for machine *C.*

The next lowest index number is 1.17 for order 4 on both machines *B* and *C.* Therefore, order 4 is assigned to machine *C.* Orders 1 and 2 are next assigned to machine *B.* This latter assignment completes the load for machine *B* with exactly 40 hours assigned. The assignments on machine *A* now require 67 hours, which means that more orders must be reassigned.

The next assignment is order 8 to machine *C,* and finally order 5 to machine *D.* The assignments by the index method are as shown in Figure 87.

The index method yields machine assignments requiring a total of 146 hours. This presents an improvement of 9 hours over the

	Hours per Order and Index Number			
	Machines			
	A	B	C	D
1	10	(12) (1.2)	18 (1.8)	25 (2.5)
2	5	(6) (1.2)	12 (2.4)	18 (3.6)
3	8	(8) (1.0)	10 (1.25)	15 (1.88)
4	12	14 (1.17)	(14) (1.17)	20 (1.67)
5	20	25 (1.25)	27 (1.35)	(35) (1.75)
6	(15)	19 (1.26)	23 (1.53)	30 (2.0)
7	14	(14) (1.0)	16 (1.14)	20 (1.43)
8	17	19 (1.12)	(25) (1.47)	27 (1.59)
9	(8)	10 (1.25)	16 (2.0)	30 (3.75)
10	(9)	12 (1.34)	18 (2.0)	25 (2.78)
Available Time	40	40	40	120
Assigned Time	32	40	39	35

Fig. 87. Index Method Assignments—Assignments Indicated by Circled Numbers

rather arbitrary assignment-as-received method. This means then that 9 more hours of work can be accomplished in the same time period. The index method in this manner can actually increase manufacturing capacity without adding any new equipment. The method is not, however, without some shortcomings. The assignments in Figure 87 can be even further improved by moving orders 3 and 7 from *B* to *C* and order 8 from *C* to *B*. This results in assignments requiring 144 hours as shown in Figure 88.

Summary. The index method, although it is little more than a formalized inspection procedure, is completely general in its application and far exceeds other inspection methods, particularly in larger problems. In the sample problem, a savings of 11 hours was rather easily realized.

One manufacturing concern uses the index method rather successfully in their automatic-screw machine department. A clerk and a scheduler, in several hours every Friday afternoon, prepare the work assignments for the following week. This involves between 100 and 200 orders or jobs assigned to somewhat more than

	Hours per Order and Index Number			
	Machines			
	A	B	C	D
1	10	**12** (1.2)	18 (1.8)	25 (2.5)
2	5	**6** (1.2)	12 (2.4)	18 (3.6)
3	8	8 (1.0)	**10** (1.25)	15 (1.88)
4	12	14 (1.17)	**14** (1.17)	20 (1.67)
5	20	25 (1.25)	27 (1.35)	**35** (1.75)
6	**15**	19 (1.26)	23 (1.53)	30 (2.0)
7	14	14 (1.0)	**16** (1.14)	20 (1.43)
8	17	**19** (1.12)	25 (1.47)	27 (1.59)
9	**8**	10 (1.25)	16 (2.0)	30 (3.75)
10	**9**	12 (1.34)	18 (2.0)	25 (2.78)
Available Time	40	40	40	120
Required Time	32	37	40	35

Fig. 88. Optimum Assignment of Orders—Total Time Required 144 Hours

130 machines. These orders represent only those jobs that have manufacturing alternatives, which constitute approximately 20 to 25 per cent of the total work load. The machines are grouped by type. Those orders with no producing alternative are assigned initially, and the available machine time is reduced accordingly. The remaining machine time is used in the index method to determine the assignments for those jobs with alternative possibilities.

Excess hours are used as the measure of the effectiveness of the machine-assignment activity. Excess hours are the time required in excess of the time on the very best machine. In the preceding problem, if every order could be run on the very best machine, the 10 orders could be manufactured in 118 hours. The initial solution, established on the assign-as-received basis, required 155 hours or 37 excess hours. Excess hours can also be expressed as a percentage of the ideal minimum time. In this case the excess hours in the initial solution represent 31.3 per cent ($37/118 = 0.313$). Before using the index method, this organization averaged about 17 per cent excess hours. Now the excess hours are about 4 per cent. The use of the index method, then, has resulted in a conservative 10 per cent increase in producing ability with the existing equipment.

The index method is superior to the simplex solution for the machine-assignment problem, in that set-up and tear-down time are included in the index method, whereas the simplex solution must either ignore set-up time or approximate set-up time. The simplex method provides a better solution when set-up time requires a minor portion of the work time or when it is entirely negligible. However, the simplex solution requires more work. The simplex array for the above problem is 14×54, presenting considerably more work to obtain the solution.

The index method offers a satisfactory solution to the problem posed by rush orders. When a rush order is received, the machine assignments can be rather easily reworked to include the rush job. This solves the problem of whether to tear down a machine for the rush order or to assign the rush order to an available machine. Often the former presents an over-all better solution.

Once the index numbers have been calculated for an order, these can be permanently recorded. With time, a general indication of the index numbers for the work assigned to one machine will emerge. This then permits almost immediate assignment of an order to its correct machine, thereby materially reducing the time required in solving the machine-assignment problem. The index method permits effective and efficient solution to the machine-assignment problem by relatively unskilled personnel.

THE NORA METHOD[37]

Essentially the nora method involves approximating the problem and solving it as a distribution problem. The nora (normalized-ratio) method can be successfully applied where set-up time is negligible. The index method cannot explore the possibilities of splitting an order and running it on two or more machines, whereas the nora method can.

The nora method is accomplished in the following steps:

1. Establish an initial solution for the assignments (via the index method).

[37] This method has been assigned various names. However the nora method name will be used here.

2. Normalize machine time according to the average index number for the orders assigned to each machine—here the machine time is reduced approximately to number of hours equivalent to that for the very best machine.

3. Establish the distribution matrix array—the array presents orders and machines. The rim conditions are the available normalized machine times and the number of hours required for each order on the very best machine. The objective is to distribute orders to minimize the machine time.

4. Solve the distribution problem.

5. Translate the distribution solution to correct time requirements.

6. Check the total time requirements.

7. Revise the rim conditions and size of the stones in the distribution matrix as may be necessary to obtain time requirements as close as possible to the available time on each machine.

The method will be further explained via the same problem used to illustrate the index method. The nora method requires an initial solution that is reasonably close to the very best solution. Hence the index method solution is usually used. The solution that will be given here is that shown in Figure 88.

In Figure 88, orders 1, 2, and 8 were assigned to machine *B*. The index numbers for these assignments are:

Order	Index No., Machine *B*
1	1.20
2	1.20
8	1.12

These index numbers indicate that 1 hour of work on machine *A* requires between 1.1 and 1.2 hours of time on machine *B*. The total available time for machine *B* must then be normalized by a factor somewhere between 1.1 and 1.2. In this case a factor of 1.15 will normalize the available time on machine *B* to approximately 35 hours.[38]

[38] To establish a distribution matrix for this problem, the difference in manufacturing time requirements must be modified so that the available time on the alternative machines is expressed in units of time equivalent to the time on the best machine. In this case, the 35 hours equivalent time on machine *B* can be interpreted as meaning that, in the 40 available hours, this machine can produce work that would require approximately 35 hours on machine *A*.

Order \ Machine	A	B	C	D	Hours Required
1	−10	−12	−18	−25	10
2	−5	−6	−12	−18	5
3	−8	−8	−10	−15	8
4	−12	−14	−14	−20	12
5	−20	−25	−27	−35	20
6	−15	−19	−23	−30	15
7	−14	−14	−16	−20	14
8	−17	−19	−25	−27	17
9	−8	−10	−16	−30	8
10	−9	−12	−18	−25	9
Dummy	0	0	0	0	111
Hours Available	40	35	34	120	229

Fig. 89. Distribution Matrix for Machine-Assignment Problem

The index numbers for the assignments on machine C are:

Order	Index No., Machine C
3	1.25
4	1.17
7	1.14

Order \ Machine	A	B	C	D	Hours Required
1	−10	−12 (10)	−18	−25	10
2	−5	−6 (5)	−12	−18	5
3	−8	−8	−10 (8)	−15	8
4	−12	−14	−14 (12)	−20	12
5	−20	−25	−27	−35 (20)	20
6	−15 (15)	−19	−23	−30	15
7	−14	−14	−16 (14)	−20	14
8	−17	−19 (17)	−25	−27	17
9	−8 (8)	−10	−16	−30	8
10	−9 (9)	−12	−18	−25	9
Dummy	0 (8)	0 (3)	0 (0)	0 (100)	111
Hours Available	40	35	34	120	229

Fig. 90. Initial Solution to Distribution Approximation

This means that the available time on machine *C* must be normalized by a factor slightly less than 1.2. This normalizing ratio will correct the 40 hours of available time to approximately 34 hours. Normalizing the last machine *D* serves no particular purpose since it is far from being fully loaded.

Order \ Machine	A	B	C	D	Hours Required
1	−10	−12 (10)	−18	−25	10
2	−5	−6 (5)	−12	−18	5
3	−8	−8	−10 (8)	−15	8
4	−12	−14	−14 (12)	−20	12
5	−20 (20)	−25	−27 eval. 0	−35	20
6	−15 (15)	−19	−23	−30	15
7	−14	−14	−16 (14)	−20 (0)	14
8	−17	−19 (8)	−25	−27 (9)	17
9	−8	−10 (8)	−16	−30	8
10	−9 (5)	−12 (4)	−18	−25	9
Dummy	0	0	0	0 (111)	111
Hours Available	40	35	34	120	229

Fig. 91. Optimum Solution to Distribution Approximation of Machine-Assignment Problem

Note: A zero water-square evaluation in square 53 indicates an equally optimum alternative solution.

These normalized machine times can be used as part of the rim conditions for the distribution matrix. The remaining rim conditions, since the problem will distribute hours of work in terms of

Order	A	B	C	D
1		12		
2		6		
3			10	
4			14	
5	20			
6	15			
7			16	
8		8.95		14.3
9		10		
10	5	5.5		
Total Time Required	40.0	42.45	40.0	14.3

Fig. 92. Actual Time Requirements with the Distribution Approximation

the time required for each order on machine *A*, are merely the number of hours per order on machine *A*. The distribution matrix for this problem is then as shown in Figure 89.

It can be seen in Figure 89 that the rim conditions have been balanced with a dummy row. The problem is now approximated in an 11 × 4 distribution matrix. The index method solution can serve as the initial solution and would appear as in Figure 90.

If the assignments initially exceed the rim conditions (the normalized machine time), then the rim conditions can be easily modified to suit. Straightforward application of the modified-distribution method solves this distribution problem in several iterations. The optimum solution is shown in Figure 91.

The solution in Figure 91 must now be translated into the true machine-time requirements. This is accomplished by multiplying the stone values from Figure 91 by the corresponding index numbers from Figure 88. The machine assignments are shown in Figure 92 and indicate the real time requirements with the assignments obtained from the distribution array.

Figure 92 indicates that the required time on machine *B* exceeds the available time by 2.45 hours. This means that the available time on machine *B* was not normalized quite correctly. This discrepancy, however, is rather easily corrected. If the rim condition for machine *B* in Figure 91 is modified to 33 hours (instead of 35), a new solution can be quickly obtained. The position of the stones

Order \ Machine	A	B	C	D	Hours Required
1	−10	−12 (10)	−18	−25	10
2	−5	−6 (5)	−12	−18	5
3	−8	−8	−10 (8)	−15	8
4	−12	−14	−14 (12)	−20	12
5	−20 (20)	−25	−27	−35	20
6	−15 (15)	−19	−23	−30	15
7	−14	−14	−16 (14)	−20 (0)	14
8	−17	−19 (6)	−25	−27 (11)	17
9	−8	−10 (8)	−16	−30	8
10	−9 (5)	−12 (4)	−18	−25	9
Dummy	0	0	0	0 (109)	109
Hours Available	40	33	34	120	227

Fig. 93. Optimum Solution to Distribution Approximation with Assignments to Machine *B* Modified

in the solution remains unchanged. Essentially then, some of the assignments made to B must be shifted to other machines. Since machines A and C are fully loaded, the excess must be shifted to machine D. This is shown in Figure 93.

The modified assignments then are again translated into the

Order	A	B	C	D
1		12		
2		6		
3			10	
4			14	
5	20			
6	15			
7			16	
8		6.7		17.4
9		10		
10	5	5.5		
Total Time Required	40.0	40.2	40	17.4

Fig. 94. Revised Machine Assignments—Changed Assignments Underlined

correct time requirements for the various machines, and are shown in Figure 94.

The revised machine assignments still indicate 0.2 hour too much assigned to machine *B*. This can be rather easily corrected by shifting the portion of order 8 from *B* to *D*. This shift can be such that order 8 will require 6.5 hours on machine *B* and 17.8 hours on machine *C*. This change results in a work load of exactly 40 hours for machines *A, B,* and *C,* and 17.8 hours for machine *D*. This means that the work can be accomplished in a total time of 137.8 machine-hours.

The initial assign-as-they-come solution required 155 machine-hours; the index method required 146 hours, and the nora method required only 137.8 machine hours. If order splitting is possible, the nora method, which required slightly more work, has resulted in a savings of 17.2 hours. This means that 17.2 hours more work can be accomplished in the same schedule period.

The water-square evaluations in the optimum solution to the distribution matrix (Fig. 91) indicated that another equally optimum solution can be obtained. It might be worth while to examine this alternative optimum solution and the resulting machine assignments.

The solution in Figure 95 yields the machine assignments shown in Figure 96.

The assignments in Figure 96 indicate an overload on machine *B*. This is corrected by shifting more of order 8 to machine *D*. At the same time it seems worth while to shift more of order 7 from

Order \ Machine	A	B	C	D	Hours Required
1	−10	−12 (10)	−18	−25	10
2	−5	−6 (5)	−12	−18	5
3	−8	−8	−10 (8)	−15	8
4	−12	−14	−14 (12)	−20	12
5	−20 (16)	−25	−27 (4)	−35	20
6	−15 (15)	−19	−23	−30	15
7	−14	−14	−16 (10)	−20 (4)	14
8	−17	−19 (12)	−25	−27 (5)	17
9	−8	−10 (8)	−16	−30	8
10	−9 (9)	−12	−18	−25	9
Dummy	0	0	0	0 (111)	111
Hours Available	40	35	34	120	229

Fig. 95. Equally Optimum Alternative Solution to Distribution Approximation of Machine-Assignment Problem

machine D to C in order to load C more fully. These adjustments are shown in Figure 97.

This alternative machine assignment results in a total required time of 134.2 hours. This assignment is even better than any of the previous assignments.

Order	A	B	C	D
1		12		
2		6		
3			10	
4			12	
5	16		5.4	
6	15			
7			11.4	5.72
8		13.4		7.95
9		10		
10	9			
Total Time Required	40.0	41.4	38.8	14.67

Fig. 96. Assignments Resulting from Alternative Solution to Distribution Approximation

Order	A	B	C	D
1		12		
2		6		
3			10	
4			12	
5	16		5.4	
6	15			
7			12.5	4.3
8		12.0		10.0
9		10		
10	9			
Total Time Required	40.0	40.0	39.9	14.3

Fig. 97. Adjusted Machine Assignments Based on Alternative Optimum Solution to Distribution Approximation

Summary. The nora method, though it requires more work, can obtain better machine assignments than any other of the approximation methods presented. In the example problem, the results of the various solutions were:

Method	Required Time, hours
Assign-as-received	155
Index method	146
Nora method	
No. 1	137.8
No. 2	134.2

The index method usually provides the best machine assignment, particularly when the orders cannot be split and run on two or more machines, and when set-up and tear-down time represent a major portion of the order time. The nora method is applicable where set-up time is negligible and orders can be split.

The nora method is actually based upon the simplex formulation of the machine-assignment problem. The simplex form of such a problem exhibits the pattern characteristic of distribution problems. The normalizing procedure accomplishes essentially the same thing as dividing rows of the simplex array by suitable numbers to obtain unity numbers or near-unity numbers in the array before establishing the distribution matrix. However, the error is considerably reduced in the nora method, since it considerably narrows the choice of the normalizing ratio.

These approximation methods, the index and nora methods, are relatively simple and can be taught to and used by people with little mathematical training. The savings may not look particularly startling, yet an improvement of several per cent in an industrial situation can result in sizable savings.

APPROXIMATE SOLUTION TO MULTIDIMENSIONAL DISTRIBUTION PROBLEMS

This method was included in the previous discussion of the distribution methods. Mention of it here is appropriate since it is an approximation method; however, it does require the use of a high-speed computer. The approximate solution to a multidimensional distribution problem is an excellent example of a situation where the solution via the simplex method may be too large to solve, and where the additional cost of the truly optimum solution is not economically justifiable.

APPROXIMATION BY BOUNDING THE VALUE OF THE OBJECTIVE FUNCTION[39]

In situations where a problem is too large to be solved with readily available methods (i.e., too large for hand solution, or too large for the available calculating equipment) an approximate solution may

[39] This is similar to the method offered by T. L. Saaty in "Approximation to the Value of the Objective Function in Linear Programming by the Method of Partitions," *Journal of Operations Research Society of America,* V. 4, No. 3, June 1956, p. 352.

be the only solution attainable. Such an approximation can be obtained after the initial simplex array is established. The method discussed here can effectively indicate the lower bounds of a minimizing objective function, and the lower bounds of a maximizing objective. In many problem situations, this information is sufficient for management decisions. Then, too, this information can be useful to evaluate the possible gains in obtaining the mathematically optimum solution to the problem. It is possible that this approximation can indicate when present operations are at or near optimum, making the formal solution to the problem unnecessary.

The method of bounding the value of the objective function consists of partitioning the matrix array and solving the smaller problems obtained. This can be most easily seen in a small example. Assume that the problem represented in Figure 98 is too large to solve conveniently,[40] or that it is desirable to determine a lower bound for the objective function to see if the complete solution is worth while or even necessary.

	85	60	70	160	140	130	0	0	0	0
	x_1	x_2	x_3	y_1	y_2	y_3	W_1	W_2	W_3	W_4
1000	2	2	2	5	5	5	1			
600	3			8				1		
200		3			8				1	
800			4			10				1

Fig. 98. Initial Simplex Array for a Problem

An initial approximation can be obtained if all but one variable at a time is assumed equal to zero. For example:

Assume

$$x_2 = x_3 = y_1 = y_2 = y_3 = W_1 = W_2 = W_3 = W_4 = 0$$

then

$$x_1 \leq 500 \text{ from the first relationship (row)}$$

or

$$x_1 \leq 200 \text{ from the second relationship}$$

[40] Actually the example is rather easily solved by the simplex method. However, it will serve to illustrate the approximation method.

This means that x_1 is limited to a maximum value of 200 units. The value of the objective function when

$$x_{.} = 200$$

is

$$\begin{aligned}\text{Profit} &= 85(200) \\ &= \$17{,}000.00\end{aligned}$$

A similar analysis for each of the remaining variables yields Table 8.

Table 8

Variable	Maximum Size	Value of Objective Function
x_1	200	\$17,000.00
x_2	$66\frac{2}{3}$	4,000.00
x_3	200	14,000.00
y_1	75	12,000.00
y_2	25	3,500.00
y_3	80	10,400.00

The smallest possible value for the objective function is the largest of the above quantities, or \$17,000.00. This, then, is the approximation based on single-column partitioning of the matrix.

Further refinements in the minimum value for the objective function can be obtained if desired by partitioning two columns and then three columns of the matrix at a time, and solving each of the smaller simple linear programming problems in turn. Here again the maximum of these individual partitions represents a new minimum value for the objective function. In fact, in this relatively simple example, the truly optimum solution is rather easily obtained, particularly after solving the two column partitions of x_1 and y_1, x_2 and y_2, and x_3 and y_3.

Summary. This method of partitioning the matrix to determine the bounds on the value of the objective function is relatively simple and permits some evaluation of a problem prior to its solution. The example used to illustrate the method involved maximizing profits. However, the method can be applied equally well to problems where costs are to be minimized. In the case of costs, the minimum of the several partitions represents the minimum value of the objective function. In other words, the costs may be more but cannot be any less. The latter result, in a cost-minimization problem can rather quickly indicate the optimality of what is being done, thereby giving an indication of the need and value of the optimum solution.

This method for bounding the objective function is very similar to the technique, suggested earlier in the book, in testing for redundant expressions in the system. In fact, the solution to the above sample problem becomes obvious when redundancy is removed. The array is reproduced in Figure 99.

	85	60	70	160	140	130	0	0	0	0
	x_1	x_2	x_3	y_1	y_2	y_3	W_1	W_2	W_3	W_4
1000	2	2	2	5	5	5	1			
600	3			8				1		
200		3			8				1	
800			4			10				1

Fig. 99. An Initial Simplex Array

An inspection of the four relationships will reveal that the first expression is not a limiting one and therefore can be eliminated. The array can then be reduced to 3×9 as shown in Figure 100.

The array in Figure 100 points to even further possible simplification. If the columns headed y_1 and y_2 are multiplied by 3/8 and the column headed y_3 multiplied by 2/5, the array is as shown in Figure 101.

	85	60	70	160	140	130	0	0	0
	x_1	x_2	x_3	y_1	y_2	y_3	W_2	W_3	W_4
600	3			8			1		
200		3			8			1	
800			4			10			1

Fig. 100. An Initial Simplex Array—Redundant Expression Removed

	85	60	70	60	52.5	52	0	0	0
	x_1	x_2	x_3	y_1	y_2	y_3	W_2	W_3	W_4
600	3			3			1		
200		3			3			1	
800			4			4			1

Fig. 101. An Initial Simplex Array—Columns y_1, y_2, and y_3 Modified

The changes from Figure 100 to 101 are valid in that one may operate upon a column or columns in the array without changing the total value of the matrix. In Figure 101, the columns y_1, y_2, and y_3 are redundant columns in that they are identical with the columns headed x_1, x_2, and x_3, except for the number in the index row. The y's stand no chance of entering a solution (since the identical x column has an algebraically larger objective number) and therefore are redundant columns. Elimination of these reduces the problem to an obvious solution, yielding a maximum profit of $35,000.00.

Summary. Several approximation methods which offer an economical means of obtaining a near-optimum solution have been presented. The index and nora methods are the most widely used of the various approximation methods, primarily owing to their applicability to machine loading and scheduling. The approximation method for multidimensional distribution problems is relatively new but can conceivably be useful for multiproduct and multiplant production planning.

Approximation methods often are tailored to a particular type of application. However, often the formulation of a problem will point to possible approximations which may make the mathematical solution uneconomical or even unnecessary. Approximate solutions are often required in industry, because of either the time requirements or the relative lack of highly trained personnel. Several of the approximation methods can be very effectively performed by relatively unskilled people with little formal mathematical training.

5. Typical Problems and Their Solution

Problems solvable by mathematical programming are usually approached in four phases:

1. Statement of the problem—a suitable word statement of the problem and the conditions that surround it.

2. Formulation—the development of a system of mathematical expressions and an objective which adequately describes the problem mathematically (this is often referred to as model construction, since in essence one is building a mathematical model of the problem).

3. Solution—application of the simplex or other suitable methods to obtain an optimum solution to the mathematical formulation of the problem.

4. Analysis—the review and interpretation of the optimum solution and its various alternatives, as courses of action to the problem. The analysis must, of course, be prepared in terms that management will readily understand.

The four phases above are fundamental to most problem-solving situations. The major difference between other methods and the operations research and mathematical programming approach is the degree to which the formulation is prepared. Here is where the major advantage is to be gained by the operations research philosophy.

The simplex method and its various ramifications are not too difficult, as could be seen in the preceding chapter. Hence the solution rarely presents a problem except one of tedium with an extremely large quantity of numbers. Therefore, the major emphasis must be directed toward formulation and analysis. This is where practice is the best means of improving formulation proficiency. This chapter will emphasize formulation and analysis via two manufacturing problems.

The problems are relatively simple—yet not so simple as to be impractical or have obvious solutions. The problems are shown in their entirety and provide a very clear step-by-step development from the statement of the problem through the complete analysis of the optimum and various alternative solutions. The first problem is one of product allocation—allocating work to be accomplished (orders) to available pieces of manufacturing equipment (processes). The second problem is one of blending available ingredients to make required amounts of paint vehicles. Blending problems are a special example of product-allocation problems in that one allocates available supplies to meet requirements of various products.

A MANUFACTURING PROBLEM

In most manufacturing situations, a number of courses of action are possible. Usually the multifacet nature of the problem defies solution by inspection or intuition. Such a manufacturing problem will be considered here.

The Problem. A manufacturer receives orders for two products (A and B). The customers require 200 units of product A and 300 units of product B. Both products are manufactured in two operations.

The first operation is performed in process I, and it requires 2 hours and 4 hours per unit to produce products A and B, respectively. The second operation can be performed in either process II or III. It requires 4 hours per unit of product A and 7 hours per unit of product B produced in process II. It requires 10 hours per unit of product A and 12 hours per unit of product B manufactured in process III. Set-up time on the various processes is negligible.

There are 1700 hours of manufacturing time on process I, 1000 hours on process II, and 3000 hours on process III available in the schedule period. An additional 500 hours is available on process II in overtime.

The labor and burden costs are \$3.00, \$3.00, and \$2.00 per hour on processes I, II, and III, respectively. The overtime on process II increases the costs to \$4.50 per hour.

If no penalty is assumed for idle machine time (assuming that the processes will be occupied with other jobs when not doing these orders), then the problem is to determine how to manufacture the products so that the over-all costs are minimum.

Formulation. The formulation of this problem will be somewhat similar to that of the problem used to illustrate the simplex method. The variables represent the various ways that a unit can be manufactured. There will be six variables in this particular problem, since there are three different ways of producing each product.

Let

x_1 = number of units of product A manufactured in process I and at straight time in process II

x_2 = number of units of product A manufactured in process I and at overtime in process II

x_3 = number of units of product A manufactured in process I and process III

x_4 = number of units of product B manufactured in process I and at straight time in process II

x_5 = number of units of product B manufactured in process I and at overtime in process II

x_6 = number of units of product B manufactured in process I and process III

The formulation will then contain four restrictions, each one representing the limitation of available time on the four processes. (Note: Here we may consider process II at overtime as essentially a different process since the costs will be different from those of process II at regular time.) These restrictions are:

$$\text{(Process I)} \qquad 2x_1 + 2x_2 + 2x_3 + 4x_4 + 4x_5 + 4x_6 \leq 1700 \qquad (5.1)$$

$$\text{(Process II: straight time)} \qquad 4x_1 + 7x_4 \leq 1000 \qquad (5.2)$$

$$\text{(Process II: overtime)} \qquad 4x_2 + 7x_5 \leq 500 \qquad (5.3)$$

$$\text{(Process III)} \qquad 10x_3 + 12x_6 \leq 3000 \qquad (5.4)$$

Then, since a definite quantity of each of the products must be made, the formulation must include a suitable statement of the required quantity for each of the products. This can be stated mathematically as follows:

$$\text{(Product } A\text{)} \qquad x_1 + x_2 + x_3 = 200 \qquad (5.5)$$
$$\text{(Product } B\text{)} \qquad x_4 + x_5 + x_6 = 300 \qquad (5.6)$$

The objective function can be obtained by multiplying the labor and burden cost per hour by the number of hours required to manufacture each of the products. This cost can be determined for each of the variables (methods of production), and will be:

$$18x_1 + 24x_2 + 26x_3 + 33x_4 + 43.5x_5 + 36x_6 = \text{minimum} \qquad (5.7)$$

This function will then accomplish the objective of minimum cost. This problem assumes material costs to be constant, regardless of the manufacturing process. The latter does not have to be constant, and in many manufacturing situations definitely is not. If material costs differed by the type of process, this then could easily be included in the objective function.

The problem formulation is now complete and adequately describes the problem. Mathematically the problem can be stated: Find the values of $x \geq 0$ such that it will maximize

$$-18x_1 - 24x_2 - 26x_3 - 33x_4 - 43.5x_5 - 36x_6$$

subject to

$$2x_1 + 2x_2 + 2x_3 + 4x_4 + 4x_5 + 4x_6 \leq 1700 \qquad (5.1)$$
$$4x_1 + 7x_4 \leq 1000 \qquad (5.2)$$
$$4x_2 + 7x_5 \leq 500 \qquad (5.3)$$
$$10x_3 + 12x_6 \leq 3000 \qquad (5.4)$$
$$x_1 + x_2 + x_3 = 200 \qquad (5.5)$$
$$x_4 + x_5 + x_6 = 300 \qquad (5.6)$$

Note that the objective function is now a maximizing one where previously it was minimizing. The objective function must be maximizing since the simplex method is an algebraically maximizing technique. To maximize a function algebraically with negative numbers is equivalent to minimizing that function, or

$$\text{Minimum } f(x) = \text{maximum } - f(x)$$

The formulation can be prepared for solution by the simplex method with the addition of suitable slack and artificial variables.

The formulation ready for solution via the simplex method is then: Maximize

$$-18x_1 - 24x_2 - 26x_3 - 33x_4 - 43.5x_5 - 36x_6 + 0 \cdot W_1 + 0 \cdot W_2 + 0 \cdot W_3 + 0 \cdot W_4 - MU_1 - MU_2 \qquad (5.7)$$

subject to

$$2x_1 + 2x_2 + 2x_3 + 4x_4 + 4x_5 + 4x_6 + W_1 = 1700 \qquad (5.8)$$

$$4x_1 + 7x_4 + W_2 = 1000 \qquad (5.9)$$

$$4x_2 + 7x_5 + W_3 = 500 \qquad (5.10)$$

$$10x_3 + 12x_6 + W_4 = 3000 \qquad (5.11)$$

$$x_1 + x_2 + x_3 + U_1 = 200 \qquad (5.12)$$

$$x_4 + x_5 + x_6 + U_2 = 300 \qquad (5.13)$$

The slack variables (W_1 through W_4) were added to make equations of the inequalities. These can be thought of as representing idle process time. The slack variables have zero weight in the objective function because no penalty is assumed for idle process time.

The artificial variables (U_1 and U_2) are included to form the square identity for the simplex method. The $-M$ cost factor (defined as so large that it dominates all else in the problem) is attached to the artificial variables to assure that they will be zero, since equality exists without them. The problem is now ready for the simplex method. The initial simplex array for this problem is as shown in Figure 102.

Solution. This problem was solved by hand in four iterations, the details of which are shown in Figure 103. When solving problems like this without a desk calculator it is often easier to retain the fractions as shown in Figure 103. This tends to eliminate or at least minimize the error inherent in rounding off numbers.

The optimum solution in terms of the initial formulation is

$x_1 = 200$	$W_1 = 100$
$x_2 = 0$	$W_2 = 0$
$x_3 = 0$	$W_3 = 350$
$x_4 = 200/7$	$W_4 = 0$
$x_5 = 150/7$	$U_1 = 0$
$x_6 = 250$	$U_2 = 0$

Minimum cost = \$14,475.00

			−18	−24	−26	−33	−43.5	−36	0	0	0	0	−M	−M		
			x_1	x_2	x_3	x_4	x_5	x_6	W_1	W_2	W_3	W_4	U_1	U_2		ck
0	W_1	1700	2	2	2	4	4	4	1							1719
0	W_2	1000	4			7				1						1012
0	W_3	500		4			7				1					512
0	W_4	3000			10			12				1				3023
−M	U_1	200	1	1	1								1			204
−M	U_2	300				1	1	1						1		304
		−500M	−M +18	−M +24	−M +26	−M +33	−M +43.5	−M +36	0	0	0	0	0	0		−506M +180.5

Fig. 102. Initial Simplex Array—Manufacturing Problem

This solution could be stated to management in reasonably non-mathematical terms as follows:

Manufacture 200 units of product *A* in processes I and II.
Manufacture 28.6 units of product *B* in processes I and II.
Manufacture 21.4 units of product *B* in process I and at overtime in process II.
Manufacture 250 units of product *B* in processes I and III.

This solution would probably be impractical since it requires portions of a unit to be made by two methods. However, the solution can easily be modified to present an entirely usable solution that would specify manufacturing:

200 units of product *A* in processes I and II
28 units of product *B* in processes I and II
22 units of product *B* in process I and at overtime in process II
250 units of product *B* in processes I and III.

This manufacturing will not be mathematically optimum but will present the practical optimum to this manufacturing problem. The total cost for this manufacturing is $14,481.00, or an increase of $6.00 over the mathematically optimum solution.

The mathematically optimum solution, shown in the stub of Table V of Figure 103, can be rather easily verified with the initial problem formulation.

Process I

$$2x_1 + 2x_2 + 2x_3 + 4x_4 + 4x_5 + 4x_6 + W_1 = 1700 \tag{5.8}$$
$$2(200) + 2(0) + 2(0) + \frac{4(200)}{7} + \frac{4(150)}{7} + 100 = 1700$$
$$1700 = 1700$$

Process II Straight Time

$$4x_1 + 7x_4 + W_2 = 1000 \tag{5.9}$$
$$4(200) + \frac{7(200)}{7} + 0 = 1000$$
$$1000 = 1000$$

Process II Overtime

$$4x_2 + 7x_5 + W_3 = 500 \tag{5.10}$$
$$\frac{7(150)}{7} + 350 = 500$$
$$500 = 500$$

Process III

$$10x_3 + 12x_6 + W_4 = 3000 \tag{5.11}$$
$$10(0) + 12(250) + 0 = 3000$$
$$3000 = 3000$$

				−18	−24	−26	−33	−43.5	−36	0	0	0	0	−M	−M	
				x_1	x_2	x_3	x_4	x_5	x_6	W_1	W_2	W_3	W_4	U_1	U_2	ck
I	0	W_1	1700	2	2	2	4	4	4	1	0	0	0	0	0	1719
	0	W_2	1000	4	0	0	7	0	0	0	1	0	0	0	0	1012
	0	W_3	500	0	4	0	0	7	0	0	0	1	0	0	0	512
	0	W_4	3000	0	0	10	0	0	12	0	0	0	1	0	0	3023
	−M	U_1	200	1	1	1	0	0	0	0	0	0	0	1	0	204
	−M	U_2	300	0	0	0	1	1	1	0	0	0	0	0	1	304
			−500M	−M +18	−M +24	−M +26	−M +33	−M +43.5	−M +36	0	0	0	0	0	0	−560M +108.5
II	0	W_1	1300	0	0	0	4	4	4	1	0	0	0	−2	0	1311
	0	W_2	200	0	−4	−4	7	0	0	0	1	0	0	−4	0	196
	0	W_3	500	0	4	0	0	7	0	0	0	1	0	0	0	512
	0	W_4	3000	0	0	10	0	0	12	0	0	0	1	0	0	3023
	−18	x_1	200	1	1	1	0	0	0	0	0	0	0	1	0	204
	−M	U_2	300	0	0	0	1	1	1	0	0	0	0	0	1	304
			−300M −3600	0	+6	+8	−M +33	−M +43.5	−M +36	0	0	0	0	M −18	0	−302M −3491.5
III	0	W_1	$\frac{8300}{7}$	0	$\frac{16}{7}$	$\frac{16}{7}$	0	4	4	1	$-\frac{4}{7}$	0	0	$\frac{2}{7}$	0	1199
	−33	x_4	$\frac{200}{7}$	0	$-\frac{4}{7}$	$-\frac{4}{7}$	1	0	0	0	$\frac{1}{7}$	0	0	$-\frac{4}{7}$	0	28
	0	W_3	500	0	4	0	0	7	0	0	0	1	0	0	0	512
	0	W_4	3000	0	0	10	0	0	12	0	0	0	1	0	0	3023
	−18	x_1	200	1	1	1	0	0	0	0	0	0	0	1	0	204
	−M	U_2	$\frac{1900}{7}$	0	$\frac{4}{7}$	$\frac{4}{7}$	0	1	1	0	$-\frac{1}{7}$	0	0	$\frac{4}{7}$	1	276
			$-\frac{1900}{7}M$ $-\frac{31,800}{7}$	0	$-\frac{4}{7}M$ $+\frac{174}{7}$	$-\frac{4M}{7}$ $+\frac{188}{7}$	0	−M +435	−M +36	0	$+\frac{M}{7}$ $-\frac{33}{7}$	0	0	$\frac{3M}{7}$ $+\frac{6}{7}$	0	−274M −4415.5

IV	0	W_1	$\frac{1300}{7}$	0	$\frac{16}{7}$	$-\frac{22}{21}$	0	4	0	1	$-\frac{4}{7}$	0	$-\frac{1}{3}$	$\frac{2}{7}$	0	$\frac{574}{3}$
	-33	x_4	$\frac{200}{7}$	0	$-\frac{4}{7}$	$-\frac{4}{7}$	1	0	0	0	$\frac{1}{7}$	0	0	$-\frac{4}{7}$	0	28
	0	W_3	500	0	4	0	0	7	0	0	0	1	0	0	0	512
	-36	x_6	250	0	0	$\frac{5}{6}$	0	0	1	0	0	0	$\frac{1}{12}$	0	0	$\frac{3023}{12}$
	-18	x_1	200	1	1	1	0	0	0	0	0	0	0	1	0	204
	$-M$	U_2	$\frac{150}{7}$	0	$\frac{4}{7}$	$-\frac{11}{22}$	0	1	0	0	$-\frac{1}{7}$	0	$-\frac{1}{12}$	$\frac{4}{7}$	1	$\frac{289}{12}$
			$-\frac{150M}{7}$	0	$-\frac{4M}{7}$	$\frac{11M}{42}$	0	$-M$ $+43.5$	0	0	$\frac{M}{7}$	0	$\frac{M}{12}$	$\frac{3M}{7}$	0	$-\frac{265M}{12}$
			$-\frac{94{,}800}{7}$		$+\frac{174}{7}$	$-\frac{132}{42}$					$-\frac{33}{7}$		-3	$+\frac{6}{7}$		$-13{,}484.5$
V	0	W_1	100	0	0	0	0	0	0	1	0	0	0	-2	-4	95
	-33	x_4	$\frac{200}{7}$	0	$-\frac{4}{7}$	$-\frac{4}{7}$	1	0	0	0	$\frac{1}{7}$	0	0	$-\frac{4}{7}$	0	28
	0	W_3	350	0	0	$\frac{11}{6}$	0	0	0	0	1	1	$\frac{7}{12}$	-4	-7	$\frac{4121}{12}$
	-36	x_6	250	0	0	$\frac{5}{6}$	0	0	1	0	0	0	$\frac{1}{12}$	0	0	$\frac{3023}{12}$
	-18	x_1	200	1	1	1	0	0	0	0	0	0	0	1	0	204
	-43.5	x_5	$\frac{150}{7}$	0	$\frac{4}{7}$	$-\frac{11}{42}$	0	1	0	0	$-\frac{1}{7}$	0	$-\frac{1}{12}$	$\frac{4}{7}$	1	$\frac{289}{12}$
			$-14{,}475$	0	0	$8\frac{1}{4}$	0	0	0	0	1.5	0	.625	M -24	M -43.5	$2M$ $-\frac{58{,}128.5}{4}$

Fig. 103. Simplex Solution to Manufacturing Problem

Number of Product A

$$\begin{aligned} x_1 + \quad x_2 + \quad x_3 &= 200 \qquad (5.12)\\ 200 + \quad 0 + \quad 0 &= 200\\ 200 &= 200 \end{aligned}$$

Number of Product B

$$\begin{aligned} x_4 + \quad x_5 + \quad x_6 &= 300 \qquad (5.13)\\ \frac{200}{7} + \quad \frac{150}{7} + \quad 250 &= 300\\ 300 &= 300 \end{aligned}$$

The optimum value for the objective function is then:

$$-18x_1 - 24x_2 - 26x_3 - 33x_4 - 43.5x_5 - 36x_6 - MU_1 - MU_2 = \text{maximum}$$

$$-18(200) - 24(0) - 26(0) - \frac{33(200)}{7} - \frac{43.5(150)}{7} - 36(250) - M\cdot 0 - M\cdot 0 = \text{maximum}$$

$$-14475 = \text{maximum}$$

Analysis. The final matrix (Table V, Fig. 103) not only provides the optimum solution but it also affords useful information, in the index row numbers, regarding alternative solutions. The index row number for every variable in the optimum solution (those variables appearing in the stub) will, of course, be zero. The remaining index row numbers provide the required information concerning alternative solutions.

The index row number for the second column is zero. This indicates that the variable in this column x_2 could be introduced into the solution without increasing the total costs of the problem. This then, would provide an equally optimum alternative solution to the problem. This optimum alternative solution (shown in Fig. 104) can be obtained by accomplishing another iteration from Table V (Fig. 103) by introducing x_2 or selecting the second column as the key column. It can be seen that the solution is different but that exactly the same total cost prevails.

The alternative solution is:

$$\begin{aligned} x_1 &= 162.5 & W_1 &= 100\\ x_2 &= 37.5 & W_2 &= 0\\ x_3 &= 0 & W_3 &= 350\\ x_4 &= 50 & W_4 &= 0\\ x_5 &= 0 & U_1 &= 0\\ x_6 &= 250 & U_2 &= 0 \end{aligned}$$

Minimum cost = \$14,475.00

which can be rather easily verified by the initial formulation.

			-18	-24	-26	-33	-43.5	-36	0	0	0	0	$-M$	$-M$	
			x_1	x_2	x_3	x_4	x_5	x_6	W_1	W_2	W_3	W_4	U_1	U_2	ck
0	W_1	100	0	0	0	0	0	0	1	0	0	0	-2	-4	95
-33	x_4	50	0	0	$-\frac{5}{6}$	1	1	0	0	0	0	$-\frac{1}{12}$	0	1	$\frac{625}{12}$
0	W_3	350	0	0	$\frac{11}{6}$	0	0	0	0	1	1	$\frac{7}{12}$	-4	-7	$\frac{4121}{12}$
-36	x_6	250	0	0	$\frac{5}{6}$	0	0	1	0	0	0	$\frac{1}{12}$	0	0	$\frac{3023}{12}$
-18	x_1	162.5	1	0	$\frac{35}{24}$	0	$-\frac{7}{4}$	0	0	$\frac{1}{4}$	0	$\frac{7}{48}$	0	$-\frac{7}{4}$	$\frac{7769}{48}$
-24	x_2	37.5	0	1	$-\frac{11}{24}$	0	$\frac{7}{4}$	0	0	$-\frac{1}{4}$	0	$-\frac{7}{48}$	1	$\frac{7}{4}$	$\frac{2023}{48}$
		$-14,475$	0	0	8.25	0	0	0	0	1.5	0	0.625	M -24	M 43.5	$2M$ -14532.125

Fig. 104. Equally Optimum Alternative Solution for Manufacturing Problem

This optimum alternative solution could be stated to management as follows:

Manufacture 162.5 units of product A on processes I and II.
Manufacture 37.5 units of product A on process I and at overtime on process II.
Manufacture 50 units of product B on processes I and II.
Manufacture 250 units of product B on processes I and III.

Or this would be somewhat more practical if it was:

Manufacture 162 units of product A on processes I and II.
Manufacture 38 units of product A on process I and at overtime on process II.
Manufacture 50 units of product B on processes I and II.
Manufacture 250 units of product B on processes I and III.

This practical optimum alternative solution would cost $14,478.00, or an increase of $3.00 over the mathematically optimum solution. This solution has $3.00 lower total cost than the previous practical optimum; however, the difference is quite insignificant. Mathematically speaking, these two optimum solutions are the two extremes of many equally optimum solutions. It would be possible to calculate many of these intermediate optimum solutions using the marginal rate of exchange between x_2 and x_5. From Table V (Fig. 103), it can be seen that this marginal rate of exchange between x_2 and x_5 is $4/7$, or four units of x_5 are equivalent to seven units of x_2. In obtaining any of the possible intermediate solutions, this rate of exchange must be used. However, in this particular problem, it is doubtful if any of the intermediate optimum solutions would be of more than academic interest.

In both the extreme optimum solutions, since the index row numbers are unchanged, essentially the same interpretation for these numbers can be applied. The index numbers under the identity can be interpreted as follows:

1.5 in W_2 column. The objective function would be algebraically reduced (the total costs would increase) by $1.50 if one W_2 were introduced into the solution. In other words, the total cost would increase by $1.50 for each idle hour allowed on process II. Similarly, the objective function can be algebraically increased (the total costs would be further reduced) by $1.50 for each additional W_2 available in the initial solution. In other words, the total costs would be reduced if the restraint of process II were relaxed, or if one more unit of time were available on process II (at regular time).

Much the same interpretation applies to the index number (0.625) under the column headed by W_4. Here the costs would be increased by \$0.625 for each hour of idle time on process III, or reduced by \$0.625 for each additional hour of time available on process III.

It is important to note that these index row numbers represent the marginal changes to be expected, and hence are applicable only within the range of the optimum solution. This is to say that the change indicated by the index row number is not valid for an unlimited change in the variables represented.

It is interesting to note in this particular problem that the solution is in no way affected if the assumption of no penalty for idle equipment time is removed. It can be easily verified that there is no change in the optimum solution if the costs of labor and burden for each process are assumed applicable to the idle time on the processes (assign -3, -3, -4.5, -2 to the slack variables W_1, W_2, W_3, and W_4, respectively, in the objective function). The only effect this will have on the optimum solution is that the optimum value of the objective function is changed from \$14,475.00 to \$15,825.00. This objective function will minimize the cost of production as well as the total cost of process idle time.

This problem could have also been solved with the modified simplex method. It is of interest to note the effect of this modified method in terms of reducing the work involved, particularly in calculating the index row numbers. Figure 105 illustrates the phase I solution to this problem reached by the modified simplex method. It can be seen that the phase I calculations obtain the optimum solution directly in this particular problem. Comparison between the solutions shown in Figures 103 and 105 will show the same number of iterations except that the index row numbers in each iteration by the modified simplex method are considerably simpler. This then increases the hand computation efficiency.

Summary. This manufacturing problem has been presented to illustrate the four phases inherent in solving a problem and to show the elementary techniques of problem formulation. Set-up time for the various processes was assumed to be negligible in the above analysis. However, this is not necessarily true of many manufacturing processes. Set-up time cannot be effectively included in the formulation since it is nonlinear (i.e., set-up time is completely independent of the quantity to be manufactured). Some work has been done in nonlinear programming, but it is beyond the scope of this book.

				0	0	0	0	0	0	0	0	0	0	−1	−1	
				x_1	x_2	x_3	x_4	x_5	x_6	W_1	W_2	W_3	W_4	U_1	U_2	ck
	0	W_1	1700	2	2	2	4	4	4	1	0	0	0	0	0	1719
	0	W_2	1000	4	0	0	7	0	0	0	1	0	0	0	0	1012
	0	W_3	500	0	4	0	0	7	0	0	0	1	0	0	0	512
I	0	W_4	3000	0	0	10	0	0	12	0	0	0	1	0	0	3023
	−1	U_1	200	1	1	1	0	0	0	0	0	0	0	1	0	204
	−1	U_2	300	0	0	0	1	1	1	0	0	0	0	0	1	304
			−500	−1	−1	−1	−1	−1	−1	0	0	0	0	0	0	−506
	0	W_1	1300	0	0	0	4	4	4	1	0	0	0	−2	0	1311
	0	W_2	200	0	−4	−4	7	0	0	0	1	0	0	−4	0	196
	0	W_3	500	0	4	0	0	7	0	0	0	1	0	0	0	512
II	0	W_4	3000	0	0	10	0	0	12	0	0	0	1	0	0	3023
	0	x_1	200	1	1	1	0	0	0	0	0	0	0	1	0	204
	−1	U_2	300	0	0	0	1	1	1	0	0	0	0	0	1	304
			−300	0	0	0	−1	−1	−1	0	0	0	0	1	0	−302
	0	W_1	$\frac{8300}{7}$	0	$\frac{16}{7}$	$\frac{16}{7}$	0	4	4	1	$-\frac{4}{7}$	0	0	$\frac{2}{7}$	0	1199
	0	x_4	$\frac{200}{7}$	0	$-\frac{4}{7}$	$-\frac{4}{7}$	1	0	0	0	$\frac{1}{7}$	0	0	$-\frac{4}{7}$	0	28
	0	W_3	500	0	4	0	0	7	0	0	0	1	0	0	0	512
III	0	W_4	3000	0	0	10	0	0	12	0	0	0	1	0	0	3023
	0	x_1	200	1	1	1	0	0	0	0	0	0	0	1	0	204
	−1	U_2	$\frac{1900}{7}$	0	$\frac{4}{7}$	$\frac{4}{7}$	0	1	1	0	$-\frac{1}{7}$	0	0	$\frac{4}{7}$	1	276
			$-\frac{1900}{7}$	0	$-\frac{4}{7}$	$-\frac{4}{7}$	0	−1	−1	0	$\frac{1}{7}$	0	0	$\frac{3}{7}$	0	−274

	0	W_1	$\frac{1300}{7}$	0	$\frac{16}{7}$	$-\frac{22}{21}$	0	4	0	1	$-\frac{4}{7}$	0	$-\frac{1}{3}$	$\frac{2}{7}$	0	$\frac{574}{3}$
	0	x_4	$\frac{200}{7}$	0	$-\frac{4}{7}$	$-\frac{4}{7}$	1	0	0	0	$\frac{1}{7}$	0	0	$-\frac{4}{7}$	0	28
	0	W_3	500	0	4	0	0	7	0	0	0	1	0	0	0	512
IV	0	x_6	250	0	0	$\frac{5}{6}$	0	0	1	0	0	0	$\frac{1}{12}$	0	0	$\frac{3023}{12}$
	0	x_1	200	1	1	1	0	0	0	0	0	0	0	1	0	204
	−1	U_2	$\frac{150}{7}$	0	$\frac{4}{7}$	$-\frac{11}{42}$	0	1	0	0	$-\frac{1}{7}$	0	$-\frac{1}{12}$	$\frac{4}{7}$	1	$\frac{289}{12}$
			$-\frac{150}{7}$	0	$-\frac{4}{7}$	$\frac{11}{42}$	0	−1	0	0	$\frac{1}{7}$	0	$\frac{1}{12}$	$\frac{3}{7}$	0	$\frac{265}{12}$
	0	W_1	100	0	0	0	0	0	0	1	0	0	0	−2	−4	95
	0	x_4	$\frac{200}{7}$	0	$-\frac{4}{7}$	$-\frac{4}{7}$	1	0	0	0	$\frac{1}{7}$	0	0	$-\frac{4}{7}$	0	28
	0	W_3	350	0	0	$\frac{11}{6}$	0	0	0	0	1	1	$\frac{7}{12}$	−4	−7	$\frac{4121}{12}$
V	0	x_6	250	0	0	$\frac{5}{6}$	0	0	1	0	0	0	$\frac{1}{12}$	0	0	$\frac{3023}{12}$
	0	x_1	200	1	1	1	0	0	0	0	0	0	0	1	0	204
	0	x_5	$\frac{150}{7}$	0	$\frac{4}{7}$	$-\frac{11}{42}$	0	1	0	0	$-\frac{1}{7}$	0	$-\frac{1}{12}$	$\frac{4}{7}$	1	$\frac{289}{12}$
			0	0	0	0	0	0	0	0	0	0	0	1	1	2

Fig. 105. Phase I Solution for Manufacturing Problem via Modified Simplex Method

One means of including set-up time is to set aside initially a portion of the available time for set-up. The mathematical analysis is then prepared with the remaining process time. In analyzing the solution, then, a comparison is made between the time initially set aside for set-up and the time actually required for set-up to accomplish the mathematical solution. Some modification and resolving may be necessary to provide the proper set-up time. This particular approach when set-up time must be considered will usually result in a near optimum but not necessarily absolutely optimum solution.

The problem developed above illustrates one of the important benefits of mathematical programming. Considerable information is provided concerning various alternative solutions, and one can quickly indicate the economics of a wide variety of alternative courses of action.

A BLENDING PROBLEM

Blending problems represent a special class of product-allocation problems. The mathematical programming analysis applied to blending problems has become a standard operating procedure in some oil refineries and in one company manufacturing livestock feeds. The problem considered here concerns blending paint vehicle.

The Problem. A company manufacturing a wide variety of paint products has one department whose sole activity is the preparation of required amounts of paint vehicle. The paint vehicle is mixed in this department before the addition of pigments, extenders, etc. Several paint vehicles are blended, and they all consist of differing amounts of oil, dryer, and thinner.

The vehicle mixing department has received orders for two blends: A and B. The orders require preparation of 400 gallons of blend A and 600 gallons of blend B. These blends must contain the following amounts of the three constituents:

	Constituents, %		
Blend	Oil	Dryer	Thinner
A	80	10	10
B	55	15	30

The orders for blends A and B must be prepared from the available stocks of constituents. The constituents are available in the pure, unmixed state in the following amounts:

Constituent	Available stock	Cost per gallon
Oil	500 gallons	$3.10
Dryer	200 gallons	$2.00
Thinner	200 gallons	$1.00

In addition to the stocks of constituents the vehicle mixing department has stocks of two commercial vehicle blends on hand. The information concerning these commercial blends is as follows:

Commercial Blend	Constituents, %			Available Stock, gallons	Cost per gallon
	Oil	Dryer	Thinner		
1	70	10	20	200	$2.50
2	40	—	60	150	1.70

The cost of preparing the orders is constant, regardless how the blends are made, and hence can be neglected. The problem is then: How should the required amounts of blends A and B be prepared from the available stocks at a minimum total cost?

Formulation. If the assumption is made that the composition of these blends is linear (i.e., that 20 gallons of constituents yields exactly 20 gallons of blend), then the problem can be solved via linear programming.

The variables in this particular problem are the amounts of the various stocks allocated to a particular blend. In other words, an answer is required that will tell how much of a particular stock is used to make a particular blend. This can be rather easily accomplished in the formulation, if we let:

x_{11} = the number of gallons of commercial blend 1 used to make blend A (the first subscript signifies blend 1; the second blend A)

x_{12} = the number of gallons of commercial blend 1 used to make blend B

x_{21} = the number of gallons of commercial blend 2 used to make blend A

x_{22} = the number of gallons of commercial blend 2 used to make blend B

o_1 = the number of gallons of straight oil used to make blend A

o_2 = the number of gallons of straight oil used to make blend B

d_1 = the number of gallons of straight dryer used to make blend A

d_2 = the number of gallons of straight dryer used to make blend B

t_1 = the number of gallons of straight thinner used to make blend A

t_2 = the number of gallons of straight thinner used to make blend B

The system of relationships describing the problem can be developed based upon these variables. Three relationships can be constructed which describe the oil, dryer, and thinner content for blend A. These are:

Blend A

Oil	$0.7x_{11} + 0.4x_{21} + o_1 = 0.8(400) = 320$	(1)
Dryer	$0.1x_{11} \qquad\qquad + d_1 = 0.1(400) = 40$	(2)
Thinner	$0.2x_{11} + 0.6x_{21} + t_1 = 0.1(400) = 40$	(3)

The first relationship can be interpreted as:

$0.7x_{11}$ (oil from blend 1) + $0.4x_{21}$ (oil from blend 2) + o_1 (amount of pure oil) = 320 (total required amount of oil in blend A)

Since x_{11} represents the total amount of blend 1, then $0.7x_{11}$ represents the oil in blend 1.

The second and third relationships can be similarly interpreted. It can be noted that an alternative formulation would be possible. The above three relationships specify the amounts of the three constituents required in blend A. The alternative formulation is one that specifies the amounts of any two constituents and the total amount of blend A. This would appear as follows:

Blend A

Oil	$0.7x_{11} + 0.4x_{21} + o_1 = 320$
Dryer	$0.1x_{11} \qquad\qquad + d_1 = 40$
Total blend	$x_{11} + x_{21} + o_1 + d_1 + t_1 = 400$

This formulation will accomplish essentially the same results as the previous formulation. However, the formulation that will be considered here will be the first one.

A similar set of relationships can be constructed for the constituents in blend B. They are:

Blend *B*

Oil	$0.7x_{12} + 0.4x_{22} + o_2 = 0.55(600) = 330$	(4)
Dryer	$0.1x_{12} + d_2 = 0.15(600) = 90$	(5)
Thinner	$0.2x_{12} + 0.6x_{22} + t_2 = 0.30(600) = 180$	(6)

The problem formulation must include the limitations brought about by the quantities of the various stocks on hand. These limitations are:

Straight oil	$o_1 + o_2 \leq 500$	(7)
Straight dryer	$d_1 + d_2 \leq 200$	(8)
Straight thinner	$t_1 + t_2 \leq 200$	(9)
Blend 1	$x_{11} + x_{12} \leq 200$	(10)
Blend 2	$x_{21} + x_{22} \leq 150$	(11)

This then completes the system that describes the problem. The objective function is one that minimizes the costs of the variables and is

$$2.5(x_{11} + x_{12}) + 1.7(x_{21} + x_{22}) + 3.1(o_1 + o_2) + 2(d_1 + d_2) + t_1 + t_2 = \text{minimum}$$

The total formulation is then expressed in 11 relationships combining 10 variables. This is, to be sure, the reverse of the usual linear programming problem in that there are more expressions than unknowns. The problem can then be stated: Maximize

$$-2.5(x_{11} + x_{12}) - 1.7(x_{21} + x_{22}) - 3.1(o_1 + o_2) - 2(d_1 + d_2) - t_1 - t_2$$

subject to

Requirements of blend *A*	$0.7x_{11} + 0.4x_{21} + o_1 = 320$	(1)
	$0.1x_{11} + d_1 = 40$	(2)
	$0.2x_{11} + 0.6x_{21} + t_1 = 40$	(3)
Requirements of blend *B*	$0.7x_{12} + 0.4x_{22} + o_2 = 330$	(4)
	$0.1x_{12} + d_2 = 90$	(5)
	$0.2x_{12} + 0.6x_{22} + t_2 = 180$	(6)
Limitations of available stocks	$o_1 + o_2 \leq 500$	(7)
	$d_1 + d_2 \leq 200$	(8)
	$t_1 + t_2 \leq 200$	(9)
	$x_{11} + x_{12} \leq 200$	(10)
	$x_{21} + x_{22} \leq 150$	(11)

The problem as it now stands presents an 11×21 array as shown in Figure 106.

Solution. This problem could be solved by either the simplex or the modified simplex method. However, solution of this problem by hand would easily require a number of hours. Therefore, this problem was solved on an IBM-650 computer. The details of this means of solution are presented in a later discussion about computers.

The optimum matrix for this blending problem was obtained in ten iterations and is as shown in Figure 107. The optimum solution is as follows:

$$\text{Minimum cost} = \$2460.00$$

$$\begin{array}{lll} x_{11} = 0 & o_1 = 320 & t_1 = 40 \\ x_{12} = 200 & o_2 = 130 & t_2 = 50 \\ x_{21} = 0 & d_1 = 40 & \\ x_{22} = 150 & d_2 = 70 & \\ W_1 = 50 & W_4 = 0 & \\ W_2 = 90 & W_5 = 0 & \\ W_3 = 110 & U_1 \cdots U_6 = 0 & \end{array}$$

In terms of the initial statement of the problem, this optimum solution can be stated:

Make blend *A* by mixing:
- 320 gallons of straight oil.
- 40 gallons of straight dryer.
- 40 gallons of straight thinner.

Make blend *B* by mixing:
- 200 gallons of blend 1.
- 150 gallons of blend 2.
- 130 gallons of straight oil.
- 70 gallons of straight dryer.
- 50 gallons of straight thinner.

This blend preparation will leave stocks of the straight constituents as follows:

Constituent	Stock on Hand, gallons
Oil	50
Dryer	90
Thinner	110

In this problem, the mathematically optimum solution is quite practical. Blending as above will provide the required amounts of

			-2.5	-2.5	-1.7	-1.7	-3.1	-3.1	-2	-2	-1	-1	$-M$	$-M$	$-M$	$-M$	$-M$	$-M$	0	0	0	0	0
			x_{11}	x_{12}	x_{21}	x_{22}	O_1	O_2	d_1	d_2	t_1	t_2	U_1	U_2	U_3	U_4	U_5	U_6	W_1	W_2	W_3	W_4	W_5
$-M$	U_1	320	0.7		0.4		1						1										
$-M$	U_2	40	0.1						1					1									
$-M$	U_3	40	0.2		0.6						1				1								
$-M$	U_4	330		0.7		0.4		1								1							
$-M$	U_5	90		0.1						1							1						
$-M$	U_6	180		0.2		0.6						1						1					
0	W_1	500					1	1											1				
0	W_2	200							1	1										1			
0	W_3	200									1	1									1		
0	W_4	200	1	1																		1	
0	W_5	150			1	1																	1

Fig. 106. Initial Simplex Array for Blending Problem

			−2.5	−2.5	−1.7	−1.7	−3.1	−3.1	−2	−2	−1	−1	$-M$	$-M$	$-M$	$-M$	$-M$	$-M$	0	0	0	0	0
			x_{11}	x_{12}	x_{21}	x_{22}	o_1	o_2	d_1	d_2	t_1	t_2	U_1	U_2	U_3	U_4	U_5	U_6	W_1	W_2	W_3	W_4	W_5
−2.5	x_{12}	200	1	1	0	0	0	0	0	0	0	0	0	0	0	0	0	0	0	0	0	1	0
−2	d_1	40	0.1	0	0	0	0	0	1	0	0	0	0	1	0	0	0	0	0	0	0	0	0
−1.7	x_{22}	150	0	0	1	1	0	0	0	0	0	0	0	0	0	0	0	0	0	0	0	0	1
−3.1	o_2	130	−0.7	0	−0.4	0	0	1	0	0	0	0	0	0	0	1	0	0	0	0	0	−0.7	−0.4
−2	d_2	70	−0.1	0	0	0	0	0	0	1	0	0	0	0	0	0	1	0	0	0	0	−0.1	0
−1	t_2	50	−0.2	0	−0.6	0	0	0	0	0	0	1	0	0	0	0	0	1	0	0	0	−0.2	−0.6
−3.1	o_1	320	0.7	0	0.4	0	1	0	0	0	0	0	1	0	0	0	0	0	0	0	0	0	0
0	W_2	90	0	0	0	0	0	0	0	0	0	0	0	−1	0	0	−1	0	0	1	0	1	0
−1	t_1	40	0.2	0	0.6	0	0	0	0	0	1	0	0	0	1	0	0	0	0	0	0	0	0
0	W_1	50	0	0	0	0	0	0	0	0	0	0	−1	0	0	−1	0	0	1	0	0	0.7	0.4
0	W_3	110	0	0	0	0	0	0	0	0	0	0	0	0	−1	0	0	−1	0	0	1	0.2	0.6
		−2460	0	0	0	0	0	0	0	0	0	0	$M - 3.1$	$M - 2$	$M - 1$	$M - 3.1$	$M - 2$	$M - 1$	0	0	0	0.07	0.14

Fig. 107. Optimum Matrix—Vehicle Blending Problem

the correct blends at a minimum cost of \$2460.00. This cost can be broken down for each blend as follows:

	Total Cost	Cost per gallon
Blend *A*	\$1112.00	\$2.78
Blend *B*	1348.00	2.247

Analysis. Analysis of the index row numbers of the optimum array yields some rather interesting alternatives. In the optimum solution, x_{11} and x_{21} are not in the solution stub of the optimum matrix; yet the index numbers are zero (columns 1 and 3 in the array). This indicates that equally optimum alternative solutions exist for this problem. In an actual manufacturing situation like that shown in this problem, it is doubtful whether time spent exploring these alternative optimum solutions would be economically justifiable. However, it is of interest to see what these alternative optimum solutions yield in terms of alternative courses of action. The two possible alternative optimum solutions are as follows:

Alternative 1	Alternative 2
$x_{11} = 200$	$x_{11} = 0$
$x_{12} = 0$	$x_{12} = 200$
$x_{21} = 0$	$x_{21} = 66\frac{2}{3}$
$x_{22} = 150$	$x_{22} = 83\frac{1}{3}$
$o_1 = 180$	$o_1 = 293\frac{1}{3}$
$o_2 = 270$	$o_2 = 156\frac{2}{3}$
$d_1 = 20$	$d_1 = 40$
$d_2 = 90$	$d_2 = 70$
$t_1 = 0$	$t_1 = 0$
$t_2 = 90$	$t_2 = 90$
$W_1 = 50$	$W_1 = 50$
$W_2 = 90$	$W_2 = 90$
$W_3 = 110$	$W_3 = 110$
$W_4 = 0$	$W_4 = 0$
$W_5 = 0$	$W_5 = 0$
$U_1 \cdots U_6 = 0$	$U_1 \cdots U_6 = 0$

These solutions would yield blending instructions as follows:

Alternative 1

Make blend *A* from:

200 gallons of blend 1.
180 gallons of straight oil.
20 gallons of straight dryer.

Make blend B from:

150 gallons of blend 2.
270 gallons of straight oil.
90 gallons of straight dryer.
90 gallons of straight thinner.

The total cost will be \$2460.00 and can be itemized as follows:

Blend	Total Cost	Cost per gallon
A	\$1098.00	\$2.745
B	1362.00	2.270

Alternative 2

Make blend A from:

66⅔ gallons of blend 2.
293⅓ gallons of straight oil.
40 gallons of straight dryer.

Make blend B from:

200 gallons of blend 1.
83⅓ gallons of blend 2.
156⅔ gallons of straight oil.
70 gallons of straight dryer.
90 gallons of straight thinner.

The total costs will be \$2460.00 and can be itemized as follows:

Blend	Total Cost	Cost per gallon
A	\$1102.66	\$2.756
B	1357.33	2.262

It can be seen that, while the total costs remain unchanged, the alternative blending programs differ widely and the costs per gallon of the two blends differs slightly from one optimum solution to another. The cost per gallon variation is less than 1½ per cent and therefore rather insignificant.

In every optimum solution the index numbers under the slack variables present some useful information. No attempt is usually made to attach any economic significance to the index numbers in columns headed by artificial variables since no useful economic significance is usually attached to artificial variables. The economic interpretation for the index numbers in the last two columns of the optimum array is as follows:

Variable W_4 Index number 0.07

The objective function would be algebraically reduced (costs would increase) by $0.07 for every gallon of blend 1 not used; or the costs would be reduced by $0.07 for every additional gallon of blend 1 that could be obtained and used.

A similar interpretation would hold true for the variable W_5 which represents a quantity of blend 2. In other words, costs could be reduced if larger stocks of blends 1 and 2 were available. Similarly, costs would be higher with smaller stocks of these blends.

This problem exhibits an interesting facet of mathematical programming in that there are many equally optimum programs presenting relatively free choice of the program actually put to use. The interpretation of the various ramifications of these solutions is more a question of economics and time than of not having the desired information available.

SUMMARY

The two problems presented here are not real industrial problems (they are, however, based upon real industrial situations). They were developed and solved to illustrate the techniques involved in formulation and analysis. In real problems, very often the major difficulties are encountered in obtaining the necessary data for the formulation and in obtaining a clear-cut statement of the objective. Often, when the nature of the objective is in doubt, several objectives may have to be investigated. This usually means solving the mathematical model (formulation) with each of several objectives and then analyzing the several solutions obtained. This approach can be used to help determine the objective in terms of its effect upon the total problem.

These two problems have been developed to illustrate the techniques of problem formulation and solution analysis. To be certain, proficiency in solving problems with mathematical programming can only come with practice. Subsequent chapters will consider other types of problems to further emphasize these techniques.

6. Computers and Mathematical Programming

In many situations, a solution to a problem must be obtained rather quickly in order to be useful. Here is one situation where an electronic computer can be most effectively used.

Electronic computers can be most easily defined as electronic devices designed to accomplish mathematical operations or to simulate systems of mathematical expressions. Electronic computers can be divided into two major classes: analog and digital. Analog computers are designed primarily to deal with continuous data. Integration, differentiation, and solving systems of differential equations are operations well suited to analog computation. Digital computers, on the other hand, deal with discrete data and perform basic arithmetic operations. Digital computers have the advantage over analog computers primarily in speed, accuracy, and memory capacity. The major advantage of electronic computers for solving problems is in their speed. Electronic computers can accomplish operations in the range of several thousand instructions every second, making them a very useful tool in many situations.

Mathematical programming calculations, since they are composed of basic mathematical operations, can be accomplished by either analog or digital computation. The fact that most of the methods are iterative, consisting of a basic set of calculation instructions that are repeated over and over again as often as necessary, is a characteristic well suited to digital computation. The greater part of mathematical programming calculations are accomplished on digital computers primarily because of accuracy and memory requirements. Hence the discussion here will be limited to the digital computer.

Many varieties and styles of digital computers are available, some commercially available and several available through various universities. Generally speaking, any digital computer accomplishes the same end result. However, the coding and programming techniques differ widely among various digital machines. This discussion will be further limited to the IBM series of digital computers since IBM has been a pioneer in the field of mathematical programming via electronic computers and since my experience has been limited to these machines. However, it should be noted that the solution methods of mathematical programming are equally well suited to any digital-type computer.

SOME IBM COMPUTER PROGRAMS

Many programs[41] exist, and more are being prepared, for mathematical programming calculations on the various types of IBM digital machines. Several of these programs will be discussed in general here.

The IBM type-604 accounting calculator, though it is not an electronic computer in the truest sense, can be effectively used to accomplish the calculations of the distribution (stepping-stone) and simplex methods. This calculator is rather limited in terms of the maximum size of a problem, and a considerable amount of card handling is usually required, since the program cannot be efficiently stored in the machine.

The IBM type-650 computer is a stored-program machine, and therefore has been widely used for linear programming calculations. Several programs have been written for the various methods. They

[41]A computer program consists of the list of steps required to solve the problem. This is usually expressed in numbers and/or symbols which the computer can understand. Computer programming essentially involves reduction of a method to its simplest form and instructing the computer in this method in terms that it understands. This is somewhat similar to writing job instructions for a very fast idiot.

differ primarily in the size of problem that can be solved and in the type of programming instructions. The newer programs reflect the advances in programming and mathematical skills since the earlier programs were written. The IBM type-701 and 704 electronic computers have much greater memory capacity and much higher speeds than the 650. These then are much better suited for solving extremely large models very rapidly.

Distribution Methods. The distribution methods (notably the stepping stone) have been programmed for the IBM electronic computers. The individual programs and the maximum size of the problem differ widely, depending upon the author of the program and the equipment that the program was designed to use.

One program prepared for the 650 will solve distribution problems up to approximately $5m + 6n \leq 2300$ with $n < 100$. This means that a distribution problem involving 100 sources of supply and approximately 340 destinations can be solved on the 650 computer. Another program written for the IBM 701 computer will solve distribution problems up to $m \times n \leq 3000$ via the stepping-stone method.

Multidimensional distribution problems can be solved via a 704 program prepared by Dr. B. A. Galler. This program can successfully solve multidimensional problems by the method discussed in Chapter 2 containing up to 20 dimensions. The limitations on the size of problem that can be solved are that the sum of the number of rows and columns in all dimensions may not exceed 900, and the product of the number of rows and columns in all dimensions may not exceed 900,000. This program accomplishes the solution of relatively large multidimensional distribution problems. However, it must be remembered that this method is an approximation to the optimum solution.

A comparison of the speed and accuracy of this 704 program was made. A test problem solved by the simplex method on the 704 required approximately 8 hours. The same problem required approximately ½ hour on the 704, using the preceding approximation method. The approximate solution was within 8 per cent of the truly optimum solution. The solution of this test problem by hand would present an almost insurmountable task.

The Simplex Method. Several programs exist for accomplishing the simplex method on the IBM 650 computer. One program can solve problems whose matrix array (including identity) can be as large as $m \times n = 30 \times 59$ or where $m(n + 1) \leq 1400$. This program was used to solve the blending problem illustrated in the preceding chapter. This blending problem illustrated the speed advantages of electronic calculation.

The blending problem presented an 11×21 array, well within the limitations of the 650 program. To solve this problem by hand would require easily 20 to 30 minutes per iteration presenting a 3½- to 5-hour job of hand calculation. To solve this problem with the 650 required:

20 minutes to code the problem or put it on input cards in the form required by the program.

25 minutes to punch and verify the input cards.

6 minutes to read in the data and program, accomplish ten iterations, and punch out the optimum matrix array on the 650 computer.

30 minutes to interpret the output cards manually, check the solution, and assemble the optimum simplex array.

In other words this problem was easily solved with the IBM 650 computer within the span of 1½ hours. This time could be further reduced by mechanical interpretation and printing of the optimum matrix. This particular program provides the variable and constant columns, the value of the objective function, and an iteration count at the end of every iteration. This information can be most useful in rechecking a problem. To be certain, this program is not without its peculiarities and some practice is necessary to attain the coding and interpretation times indicated.

A program is available for the 650 computer that will solve problems containing up to 97 relationships, combining virtually unlimited numbers of unknowns. Another program will solve up to 40 relationships combining a virtually unlimited number of variables, whereas still another will solve up to 33 relationships combining up to 1000 variables. Each of these programs differ in the format of the input and output data and in the time required per iteration, but all of them accomplish the calculations required by the simplex method. The particular program one would use depends primarily upon the probable size and frequency of problems encountered. In solving problems encountered in an introductory course in mathematical programming, I find that the first program, which solves problems up to 30×59, is most satisfactory. The coding requirements and subsequent card handling are relatively simple and easily taught to those unfamiliar with computer programming.

The IBM type-701 computer has been programmed to solve problems up to 50×100 in matrix size via the simplex method. Two problems were calculated for me on a 701 to obtain time comparisons between hand and electronic computation. The first problem represented by a 6×18 array required 6 minutes to accomplish six iterations. Another problem in a 9×27 array required 9 minutes to accomplish ten iterations. These problems, while they show the speed attainable, are not really suitable for 701 solution, primarily because they are so small. In fact, it is almost an insult to the 701 to present such a small problem to it. The advantages of electronic computation are much better shown with larger problems.

The preceding two problems were solved at a cost of approximately $100.00. This then would not compare too favorably with the cost of approximately 8 man-hours for hand solution. Here then the cost as well as the time factors must be considered to evaluate properly the economics of hand versus electronic calculation.

The IBM type-704 computer has been programmed to solve problems containing up to 255 relationships, combining a virtually unlimited number of variables, with the modified simplex method. This program illustrates the advances in computational efficiency over earlier programs and makes full use of the abilities and speed of the 704 computer. Certainly one must be well into the field of mathematical programming to encounter problems of the magnitude solvable by the 704 computer.

SUMMARY

Electronic digital computers, regardless of their make, can be very usefully employed to solve mathematical programming problems. Cost too is a consideration, usually a most important one, which, of course, cannot be overlooked. Computation facilities in most cases would be most difficult to justify for accomplishing only mathematical programming calculations. However electronic computers are useful in a wide range of business applications and are becoming more widely used all the time. IBM and other organizations provide facilities at various computation centers which are available on an individual problem basis.

In commerce and industry, where answers may be required in a minimum time and where problems may be very large, the electronic computer is an invaluable tool, providing solutions rapidly, economically, and completely free from human error inherent in hand calculation. In education, particularly in the field of mathematical programming, the electronic computer can be used to minimize the actual solution time, so that more emphasis can be placed upon problem formulation and the analysis of the optimum solution. This can be a very useful teaching tool, providing in minutes what would take hours to accomplish by hand.

7. Production Planning[42]

At present, the function of production planning in industry is a somewhat inexact activity that strives by various means to develop a broad over-all producing plan for an organization. This is management's grand strategy planning. In developing such a plan, an incomplete picture of the cost relationships usually exists, and in many cases it is difficult to obtain a factual comparison between two or more production plans.

The production planning activity includes the consideration of various tangible factors (producing ability, costs, etc.) and intangible factors (labor and community relations, management policies, etc.) and the analysis of their effects upon the manufacturing plan and vice versa. This is usually accomplished in an intuitive manner, somewhat like putting all the information into a stew pot and

---

[42] I am indebted to Mr. N. V. Reinfeld of Executive Services, Cleveland, Ohio, who suggested this general approach to the production planning problem. A similar approach may be found in: Joseph O. Harrison Jr., "Linear Programming and Operations Research," J. F. McCloskey and F. N. Trefethen, eds, *Operations Research for Management,* pp. 231–33, John Hopkins Press, 1954, and Edward H. Bowman, "Production Scheduling by the Transportation Method of Linear Programming," *Journal of the Operations Research Society of America,* V. 4, No. 1, February 1956, pp. 100–103.

cooking up a "brew" (manufacturing plan) that is probably somewhat similar to last year's because everyone was reasonably satisfied with last year's plan. Mathematical programming offers a more scientific and potentially better approach to the production planning problem.

The mathematical programming approach is accomplished in two phases. The first phase considers only the tangible cost and capacity data. Here it is possible to consider the problem as one of distributing producing ability to meet a sales demand at the lowest possible cost. The solution to the first phase of the problem may be obtained via the distribution methods of mathematical programming. The second phase of this approach involves analysis of the lowest-cost plan of the first phase in terms of its effect upon the established management policies of the organization and vice versa. The plan is then modified as may be necessary, but the cost factors are still included, permitting modifications to be accomplished in the lowest-cost manner. This approach then results in the lowest-cost manufacturing plan that is consistent with the various organizational limitations and policies.

GENERAL MATHEMATICAL FORMULATION

Before developing a specific problem it will be of interest to consider the general mathematical expression for a production planning problem.

If we let

P_j = number of units of producing capacity in the jth month

Q_i = number of units of forecasted sales for the ith month

x_{ij} = number of units produced in the jth month and sold in the ith month

a_{ij} = cost per unit to produce in the jth month and inventory for sales demand in the ith month

$i = (1, 2, 3, \cdots, 12)$

$j = (1, 2, 3, \cdots, 12)$

then the production planning problem can be formulated in two sets of relationships. The first set (restrictions) says that what is produced in the jth month and sold in that month and succeeding months is less-than-or-equal-to the production capacity for the jth month. Mathematically, this is

$$\sum_{i=j}^{12} x_{ij} \leq P_j \tag{7.1}$$

where

$$i \geq j$$

The second set of relationships (equations) considers the sales demand. What is sold in the ith month must, of course, be produced in that month or preceding months (since back orders will be excluded from consideration). Mathematically, this is

$$\sum_{j=1}^{i} x_{ij} = Q_i \tag{7.2}$$

The objective function is to minimize the producing and storage costs and can be stated thus:

$$\sum_{\substack{i=1 \\ j=1}}^{12} (a_{ij} x_{ij}) = \text{minimum} \tag{7.3}$$

The total producing capacity is then

$$\sum_{j=1}^{12} P_j = P_{\text{tot}} \tag{7.4}$$

and the total sales forecast is then

$$\sum_{i=1}^{12} Q_i = Q_{\text{tot}} \tag{7.5}$$

where

$$P_{\text{tot}} \geq Q_{\text{tot}}$$

The total producing capacity (P_{tot}) is shown as greater than the total sales demand (Q_{tot}). This will be the usual case and can be obtained by including overtime producing capacity and/or subcontracting. The latter offers a potentially unlimited producing capacity.

The summation limits of (7.1) and (7.2) factor out the possibility of back orders; i.e., February's production cannot be used to fulfill the January sales demand. Back orders may be considered if management can provide factual cost information. However, this general statement of the problem will not allow back orders since it is usually difficult if not impossible to assign a factual cost to back orders, and also since the sales forecast is usually considered as a demand that must at least be met.

The preceding general formulation as it stands is really not as general as it can be. Usually overtime production must be included since it may indeed be more economical to manufacture at overtime to meet a demand rather than manufacturing at regular time with subsequent inventories to meet the demand. The general formulation can be expanded to include this if we let

x_{ij} = number of units produced at straight time in the jth month and sold in the ith month

x'_{ij} = number of units produced at time-and-one-half overtime in the jth month and sold in the ith month

x''_{ij} = number of units produced at double overtime in the jth month and sold in the ith month

a_{ij} = cost per unit to produce at straight time in the jth month and inventory for sales demand in the ith month

a'_{ij} = cost per unit to produce at time-and-one-half overtime in the jth month and inventory for sales demand in the ith month

a''_{ij} = cost per unit to produce at double overtime in the jth month and inventory for sales demand in the ith month

P_j = number of units of straight-time producing capacity in the jth month

P'_j = number of units of time-and-one-half overtime producing capacity in the jth month

P''_j = number of units of double overtime producing capacity in the jth month

Q_i = number of units of forecasted sales in the ith month

$j = (1, 2, 3, \cdots, 12)$

$i = (1, 2, 3, \cdots, 12)$

Then the first set of restrictions involving producing capacities can be expanded to include the overtime consideration as follows:

$$\sum_{i=j}^{12} x_{ij} \leq P_j \tag{7.6}$$

$$\sum_{i=j}^{12} x'_{ij} \leq P'_j \tag{7.7}$$

$$\sum_{i=j}^{12} x''_{ij} \leq P''_j \tag{7.8}$$

The second set of relationships (equations) expressing the sales demand can also be expanded thus:

$$\sum_{j=1}^{i} (x_{ij} + x'_{ij} + x''_{ij}) = Q_i \tag{7.9}$$

and the expanded form of the objective function is now

$$\sum_{\substack{i=1\\j=1}}^{12} (a_{ij}x_{ij} + a'_{ij}x'_{ij} + a''_{ij}x''_{ij}) = \text{minimum} \tag{7.10}$$

The objective function (7.8) can be simplified somewhat by deducting the basic unit costs in direct material, direct labor, and burden or overhead, since these are common to every unit produced. These costs will remain constant with any fixed total demand. The true variable costs in the problem are labor overtime premium, storage and inventory costs, and hence are the only costs that need to appear in the objective function.

This general formulation or mathematical model of the production planning problem takes the form of 12 linear equations and 36 linear inequalities involving 234 variables. At this point the problem might seem insurmountable since the simplex method would require a 48 × 282 matrix array (48 relationships or rows and 234 variables or columns plus a 48 × 48 identity). However, the simplex array would contain all unity numbers, and hence would indicate a type of distribution problem. The simplex array would not, however, exhibit the regular pattern of numbers so characteristic of distribution problems.

The distribution problem pattern in the simplex array would be more readily seen if the summation limits (relationships 7.6, 7.7, 7.8 and 7.9) were relaxed so that

$$\sum_{i=1}^{12} x_{ij} \leq P_j \tag{7.6.1}$$

$$\sum_{i=1}^{12} x'_{ij} \leq P'_j \tag{7.7.1}$$

$$\sum_{i=1}^{12} x''_{ij} \leq P''_j \tag{7.8.1}$$

and

$$\sum_{j=1}^{12} (x_{ij} + x'_{ij} + x''_{ij}) = Q_i \tag{7.9.1}$$

This would be an equally legitimate formulation so long as an arbitrarily large cost (like $-M$) were assigned to all x_{ij}'s where $i < j$. This second formulation would result in a 48×480 simplex matrix (48 relationships with 432 variables plus a 48×48 identity). Though this formulation would result in an even larger array than the previous one, it would exhibit the regular pattern so characteristic of distribution problems.

Therefore, the production planning problem lends itself to solution as a distribution problem. The factory capacities month by month can be considered as sources of supply whereas the sales forecast can be considered as demand. With this analogy it is possible to visualize a distribution matrix with monthly factory capacities represented by the columns and the monthly sales forecast represented by the rows. This may be more readily seen in a typical problem.

A PROBLEM

An organization, producing a variety of home workshop machines, desires an annual manufacturing plan to be prepared for a combination disk and belt sanding machine. The sales forecast and all pertinent cost and capacity data are available. The planning is best accomplished by working with man-hour data because this is the most reliable measure of producing capacity.

The problem is complicated to some extent because the manufacturing plans are already prepared for all products except this sanding machine. This means that a portion of the total factory capacity is already taken up in producing these other products. Therefore, the available capacity shows a considerable fluctuation during the year.

The problem is then to develop the best producing plan (i.e., the lowest-cost plan consistent with management's policies) to meet the sales forecast for the sanding machine.

Data. The following data are representative of that required to develop such a manufacturing plan:

1. Forecasted sales in units:

January	12,500	July	25,000
February	7,500	August	27,500
March	17,500	September	32,500
April	22,500	October	30,000
May	17,500	November	22,500
June	20,000	December	15,000
	Total	250,000 units[43]	

2. The factory capacity already planned for the other products is as follows:

	Man-hours		Man-hours
January	46,000	July	48,000
February	53,000	August	41,000
March	38,000	September	30,000
April	44,000	October	48,000
May	44,000	November	48,000
June	42,000	December	49,000

3. The factory normally works two shifts of 40 hours per week, 52 weeks per year. The two shifts are of equal size.

4. In a normal two-shift working day the total plant capacity is 3520 man-hours.

5. Each unit of the sanding machine requires 1.5 man-hours of direct labor. This includes necessary plant efficiency allowances.

[43] This forecast is by no means to be construed as indicative of the actual demand for this type of product. This is merely an illustrative problem.

6. The average direct labor costs are:

First shift	$1.70 per hour
Second shift	$1.75 per hour

7. The average factory burden is determined as 200 per cent of the direct labor costs.

8. Each unit requires $10.00 of direct materials.

9. Overtime is paid at time and one-half for work in excess of 8 hours in one day and 40 hours in one week. Overtime is paid at double time for sundays and holidays.

10. Storage facilities are sufficient and cost $0.20 per square foot per month. Each finished unit occupies 1.3 square feet of floor space, but the units can be stacked four high.

11. Inventory charges are 20 per cent per annum on the average inventory investment. Inventory charges are usually calculated monthly.

12. Finished stock inventory at the end of the producing year must not exceed 500 units.

13. Production and distribution are such that the total units produced in January are available for sale in January. The lead time from manufacturing to the consumer is zero.

This is representative of the type of data required for production planning; however, some calculations have to be accomplished before the problem is ready for mathematical programming.

First, it is necessary to determine the available plant capacity. This can be accomplished rather easily as is shown in Figure 108.

Similar calculations are necessary for every month in the planning period (one year in this case). These calculations are summarized for the entire year in Figure 109. Actually only the calculations to the columns labeled available capacity are necessary to establish the rim conditions of the distribution matrix. The other data were compiled for comparative purposes. The data in Figure 109 are representative of those usually required in other methods of production planning. Usually the production plan is prepared by intuitive judgment and inspection of the data. One can see, however, that overtime production will enter into the problem because the available straight-time producing capacity is 10,296 units short of the sales forecast.

Calculations similar to those shown in Figure 108 and summarized in Figure 109 must then be made for overtime production capacity. Here it is necessary to consider either an arbitrary or a practical limitation on possible overtime. In this problem the

Month

January 1957

Regular Working Days

22

Total Plant Capacity

3520 Man-hours per day × 22 days = 77,440 man-hours
Capacity not available 46,000 man-hours
Capacity available 31,440 man-hours

$$\frac{31{,}440 \text{ man-hours}}{1.5 \text{ man-hours per unit}} = 20{,}960 \text{ units}$$

Required Capacity (Sales Forecast)

12,500 units
18,750 man-hours

Difference between Available and Required Capacity

+12,690 man-hours
+8,460 units (surplus over required capacity)

Number of Employes

$$\frac{31{,}440 \text{ man-hours}}{22(8) \text{ hours per man}} = 179 \text{ employes}$$

Fig. 108. Straight-Time Production Capacity—Sample Calculations

maximum limitation on time-and-one-half overtime was assumed to be approximately 18 hours per week or 2 hours per week day and 8 hours per Saturday. The problem solution shows that considerable latitude is possible in the maximum overtime capacity. The necessary overtime calculations for this problem are shown in Figure 110 and summarized in Figure 111. Subcontracting is omitted from this problem for simplification. Now the rim conditions for the distribution matrix are completed.

The manufacturing costs at straight time and overtime and inventory costs for several periods must be determined. Sample calculations for manufacturing costs are shown in Figure 112, and for inventory and storage costs in Figure 113.

These costs are summarized in Figure 114. In Figure 114, the basic unit cost ($17.764) has been subtracted from all the successive unit costs. The difference then reflects the overtime, inventory, and storage costs: the true variable costs. It can be seen that the inventory and storage costs are added to the investment. This

	Days	Sat.	Sun.	Total Capacity	Capacity not Available,	Available Capacity		Required Capacity		Difference		No. Employed	Cumulative Inventory
				Man-hours	Man-hours	Man-hours	Units	Man-hours	Units	Man-hours	Units		
January	22	4	4	77,440	46,000	31,440	20,960	18,750	12,500	+12,690	+ 8,460	179	+ 8,460
February	20	4	4	70,400	53,000	17,400	11,600	11,250	7,500	+ 6,150	+ 4,100	108	+12,560
March	21	5	5	73,920	38,000	35,920	23,946	26,250	17,500	+ 9,670	+ 6,446	214	+19,006
April	21	4	4	73,920	44,000	29,920	19,946	33,750	22,500	− 3,830	− 2,554	178	+16,452
May	22	4	4	77,440	44,000	33,440	22,293	26,250	17,500	+ 7,190	+ 4,793	192	+21,245
June	20	5	5	70,400	42,000	28,400	18,933	30,000	20,000	− 1,600	− 1,067	178	+20,178
July	22	4	4	77,440	48,000	29,440	19,627	37,500	25,000	− 8,060	− 5,373	167	+14,805
August	22	5	4	77,440	41,000	36,440	24,293	41,250	27,500	− 4,810	− 3,207	207	+11,598
September	20	4	5	70,400	30,000	40,400	26,933	48,750	32,500	− 8,350	− 5,567	253	+ 6,031
October	23	4	4	80,960	48,000	32,960	21,973	45,000	30,000	−12,040	− 8,027	179	− 1,996
November	20	5	4	70,400	48,000	22,400	14,933	33,750	22,500	−11,350	− 7,567	140	− 9,563
December	20	4	5	70,400	49,000	21,400	14,267	22,500	15,000	− 1,100	− 733	122	−10,296
Total							239,704		250,000		−10,296		−10,296

Fig. 109. Data for Production Plan—1957. Straight-Time Production Capacity

Month

January, 1957

Regular Work Days

22

Overtime Work Days

Saturdays—4
Sundays —4

Number of Employes

179

Units at Time-and-one-half Overtime

22 days at 2 hours per day	= 44 hours
4 Saturdays at 8 hours per day	= 32 hours
Total	76 hours
179 men at 76 hours	= 13,604 Man-hours
$\frac{\text{13,604 man-hours}}{\text{1.5 man-hours per unit}}$	= 9069 units

Units at Double-time Overtime

4 Sundays at 8 hours per day	= 32 hours
179 men at 32 hours	= 5728 man-hours
$\frac{\text{5728 man-hours}}{\text{1.5 man-hours per unit}}$	= 3819 units

Fig. 110. Overtime Production Capacity—Sample Calculations

makes, in effect, a cumulative or compound inventory charge. This need not be so and will be discussed more fully later.

These data then permit the development of a distribution matrix which expresses the first phase of the production planning problem. The problem takes the form of a 13×36 distribution matrix as shown in Figure 115.

This organization certainly makes the problem appear more easily solvable, and yet every relationship of the general statement of the problem (7.6, 7.7, 7.8, 7.9) remains intact in the problem. The producing capacity (7.6, 7.7, 7.8) is represented as the columns, and the sales demand (7.9) is represented as the rows. The simplified form of the cost factors (a_{ij}, a'_{ij}, a''_{ij} representing overtime, storage, and inventory costs) appears as the cost factors in the respective ith rows and jth columns. The quantities x_{ij}, x'_{ij}, x''_{ij} are to be determined subject to the rim conditions.

	No. Employed	Work Days	Time-and-one-half Overtime				Double-time Overtime			
			Saturday	Hours	Man-Hours	Units	Sunday	Hours	Man-Hours	Units
January	179	22	4	76	13,604	9,069	4	32	5,728	3819
February	108	20	4	72	7,756	5,170	4	32	3,456	2304
March	214	21	5	82	17,548	11,699	5	40	8,560	5706
April	178	21	4	74	13,172	8,781	4	32	5,696	3797
May	192	22	4	76	14,592	9,728	4	32	6,144	4096
June	178	20	5	80	14,240	9,493	5	40	7,120	4746
July	167	22	4	76	12,692	8,461	4	32	5,344	3562
August	207	22	5	84	17,388	11,592	4	32	6,624	4416
September	253	20	4	72	18,216	12,077	5	40	10,120	6746
October	179	23	4	78	13,962	9,308	4	32	5,728	3818
November	140	20	5	80	11,200	7,466	4	32	4,480	2986
December	122	20	4	72	8,784	5,876	5	40	4,880	3253

*Overtime determined as follows:
Time and one-half—18 hours per week.
Double time —8 hours per Sunday.

Fig. 111. Data for Production Plan—1957. Overtime Production Capacity

Straight-Time Production Costs		
Direct material	$10.00	
Direct labor 1.5 man-hours per unit × $1.725 per man-hour	2.588	
Manufacturing burden (200% direct labor)	5.176	
Total unit cost		$17.764

Time-and-one-half Overtime Production Costs		
Direct material	$10.00	
Direct labor (including overtime) 1.5 man-hours per unit × 1.5 ($1.725 per man-hour)	3.882	
Manufacturing burden*	5.176	
Total unit cost		$19.058

Double-time Overtime Production Costs		
Direct material	$10.00	
Direct labor 1.5 man-hours per unit × 2 ($1.725)	5.176	
Manufacturing burden*	5.176	
Total unit cost		$20.352

Fig. 112. Manufacturing Cost Calculations

* Note: Manufacturing burden rate would actually be lower at other than straight time. For simplicity, the same number of dollars of burden is used. This reflects the lower rate.

Unit cost		$17.764
One month's storage		
Inventory charges		
0.20 per year $\left(\frac{1 \text{ year}}{12 \text{ months}}\right)$ \$17.764	= 0.296	
Floor-space costs		
$\frac{1.3 \text{ square feet}}{4 \text{ units}}$ (\$.20 per square foot per month)	= 0.065	
Total inventory and floor-space charges		0.361
Total unit cost (including one month's storage)		$18.125

Fig. 113. Storage and Inventory Cost Calculation

Note: Inventory charges for the second month are based on the unit cost of $18.125. Subsequent inventory charges are based on the unit cost including applicable storage charges.

	Cost at Straight Time	Difference from U. C. = 17.764	Cost at Time-and-one-half Overtime	Difference from U. C. = 17.764	Cost at Double-time Overtime	Difference from U. C. = 17.764
	17.764		19.058	1.294	20.352	2.588
First Month Storage						
Inventory cost	0.296		0.318		0.339	
Floor-space cost	0.065		0.065		0.065	
	18.125	0.361	19.441	1.677	20.756	2.992
Second Month Storage						
Inventory cost	0.302		0.324		0.366	
Floor-space cost	0.065		0.065		0.065	
	18.492	0.728	19.830	2.066	21.187	3.423
Third Month Storage						
Inventory cost	0.308		0.331		0.353	
Floor-space cost	0.065		0.065		0.065	
	18.865	1.101	20.226	2.462	21.605	3.841
Fourth Month Storage						
Inventory cost	0.314		0.337		0.343	
Floor-space cost	0.065		0.065		0.065	
	19.244	1.480	20.628	2.864	22.013	4.249
Fifth Month Storage						
Inventory cost	0.321		0.344		0.368	
Floor-space cost	0.065		0.065		0.065	
	19.630	1.866	21.037	3.273	22.446	4.682
Sixth Month Storage						
Inventory cost	0.327		0.351		0.374	
Floor-space cost	0.065		0.065		0.065	
	20.022	2.258	21.453	3.689	22.885	5.121
Seventh Month Storage						
Inventory cost	0.333		0.358		0.381	
Floor-space cost	0.065		0.065		0.065	
	20.420	2.656	21.876	4.112	23.331	5.567
Eighth Month Storage						
Inventory cost	0.340		0.365		0.389	
Floor-space cost	0.065		0.065		0.065	
	20.825	3.061	22.306	4.542	23.785	6.021
Ninth Month Storage						
Inventory cost	0.347		0.372		0.396	
Floor-space cost	0.065		0.065		0.065	
	21.237	3.473	22.743	4.979	24.246	6.482
Tenth Month Storage						
Inventory cost	0.354		0.379		0.404	
Floor-space cost	0.065		0.065		0.065	
	21.656	3.892	23.187	5.423	24.715	6.951
Eleventh Month Storage						
Inventory cost	0.361		0.386		0.412	
Floor-space cost	0.065		0.065		0.065	
	22.082	4.318	23.638	5.874	25.192	7.428

Fig. 114. Unit Costs for Inventory and Storage

Sales Month \ Production Month	Jan. '57			Feb. '57			Mar. '57			Apr. '57			May '57			June '57		
	Straight-Time Production	Production at Time and One Half	Production at Double Time	Straight-Time Production	Production at Time and One Half	Production at Double Time	Straight-Time Production	Production at Time and One Half	Production at Double Time	Straight-Time Production	Production at Time and One Half	Production at Double Time	Straight-Time Production	Production at Time and One Half	Production at Double Time	Straight-Time Production	Production at Time and One Half	Production at Double Time
Jan. '57	0	−1.294	−2.588	−M	−M	−M	−M	−M	−M	−M	−M	−M	−M	−M	−M	−M	−M	−M
Feb. '57	−0.361	−1.677	−2.992	0	−1.294	−2.588	−M	−M	−M	−M	−M	−M	−M	−M	−M	−M	−M	−M
Mar. '57	−0.728	−2.066	−3.423	−0.361	−1.677	−2.992	0	−1.294	−2.588	−M	−M	−M	−M	−M	−M	−M	−M	−M
Apr. '57	−1.101	−2.462	−3.841	−0.728	−2.066	−3.423	−0.361	−1.677	−2.992	0	−1.294	−2.588	−M	−M	−M	−M	−M	−M
May '57	−1.480	−2.864	−4.249	−1.101	−2.462	−3.841	−0.728	−2.066	−3.423	−0.361	−1.677	−2.992	0	−1.294	−2.588	−M	−M	−M
June '57	−1.866	−3.273	−4.682	−1.480	−2.864	−4.249	−1.101	−2.462	−3.841	−0.728	−2.066	−3.423	−0.361	−1.677	−2.992	0	−1.294	−2.588
July '57	−2.258	−3.689	−5.121	−1.866	−3.273	−4.682	−1.480	−2.864	−4.249	−1.101	−2.462	−3.841	−0.728	−2.066	−3.423	−0.361	−1.677	−2.992
Aug. '57	−2.656	−4.112	−5.567	−2.258	−3.689	−5.121	−1.866	−3.273	−4.682	−1.480	−2.864	−4.249	−1.101	−2.462	−3.841	−0.728	−2.066	−3.423
Sept. '57	−3.061	−4.542	−6.021	−2.656	−4.112	−5.567	−2.258	−3.689	−5.121	−1.866	−3.273	−4.682	−1.480	−2.864	−4.249	−1.101	−2.462	−3.841
Oct. '57	−3.473	−4.979	−6.482	−3.061	−4.542	−6.021	−2.656	−4.112	−5.567	−2.258	−3.689	−5.121	−1.866	−3.273	−4.682	−1.480	−2.864	−4.249
Nov. '57	−3.892	−5.423	−6.951	−3.473	−4.979	−6.482	−3.061	−4.542	−6.021	−2.656	−4.112	−5.567	−2.258	−3.689	−5.121	−1.866	−3.273	−4.682
Dec. '57	−4.318	−5.874	−7.428	−3.892	−5.423	−6.951	−3.473	−4.979	−6.482	−3.061	−4.542	−6.021	−2.656	−4.112	−5.567	−2.258	−3.689	−5.121
Dummy	0	0	0	0	0	0	0	0	0	0	0	0	0	0	0	0	0	0
Total	20,960	9069	3819	11,600	5170	2304	23,946	11,699	5706	19,946	8781	3797	22,293	9728	4096	18,933	9493	4746

Production Month / Sales Month	July '57			Aug. '57			Sept. '57			Oct. '57			Nov. '57			Dec. '57			Total
	Straight-Time Production	Production at Time and One Half	Production at Double Time	Straight-Time Production	Production at Time and One Half	Production at Double Time	Straight-Time Production	Production at Time and One Half	Production at Double Time	Straight-Time Production	Production at Time and One Half	Production at Double Time	Straight-Time Production	Production at Time and One Half	Production at Double Time	Straight-Time Production	Production at Time and One Half	Production at Double Time	
Jan. '57	−M	−M	−M	−M	−M	−M	−M	−M	−M	−M	−M	−M	−M	−M	−M	−M	−M	−M	12,500
Feb. '57	−M	−M	−M	−M	−M	−M	−M	−M	−M	−M	−M	−M	−M	−M	−M	−M	−M	−M	7,500
Mar. '57	−M	−M	−M	−M	−M	−M	−M	−M	−M	−M	−M	−M	−M	−M	−M	−M	−M	−M	17,500
Apr. '57	−M	−M	−M	−M	−M	−M	−M	−M	−M	−M	−M	−M	−M	−M	−M	−M	−M	−M	22,500
May '57	−M	−M	−M	−M	−M	−M	−M	−M	−M	−M	−M	−M	−M	−M	−M	−M	−M	−M	17,500
June '57	−M	−M	−M	−M	−M	−M	−M	−M	−M	−M	−M	−M	−M	−M	−M	−M	−M	−M	20,000
July '57	0	−1.294	−2.588	−M	−M	−M	−M	−M	−M	−M	−M	−M	−M	−M	−M	−M	−M	−M	25,000
Aug. '57	−0.361	−1.677	−2.992	0	−1.294	−2.588	−M	−M	−M	−M	−M	−M	−M	−M	−M	−M	−M	−M	27,500
Sept. '57	−0.728	−2.066	−3.423	−0.361	−1.677	−2.992	0	−1.294	−2.588	−M	−M	−M	−M	−M	−M	−M	−M	−M	32,500
Oct. '57	−1.101	−2.462	−3.841	−0.728	−2.066	−3.423	−0.361	−1.677	−2.992	0	−1.294	−2.588	−M	−M	−M	−M	−M	−M	30,000
Nov. '57	−1.480	−2.864	−4.249	−1.101	−2.462	−3.841	−0.728	−2.066	−3.423	−0.361	−1.677	−2.992	0	−1.294	−2.588	−M	−M	−M	22,500
Dec. '57	−1.866	−3.273	−4.682	−1.480	−2.864	−4.249	−1.101	−2.462	−3.841	−0.728	−2.066	−3.423	−0.361	−1.677	−2.992	0	−1.294	−2.588	15,000
Dummy	0	0	0	0	0	0	0	0	0	0	0	0	0	0	0	0	0	0	147,673
Total	19,627	8461	3562	24,293	11,592	4416	26,933	12,077	6746	21,973	9308	3818	14,933	7466	2986	14,267	5876	3253	397,673

Fig. 115. Distribution Matrix—Production Planning Problem

Production Month / Sales Month	Jan. '57			Feb. '57			Mar. '57			Apr. '57			May '57			June '57		
	Straight-Time Production	Production at Time and One Half	Production at Double Time	Straight-Time Production	Production at Time and One Half	Production at Double Time	Straight-Time Production	Production at Time and One Half	Production at Double Time	Straight-Time Production	Production at Time and One Half	Production at Double Time	Straight-Time Production	Production at Time and One Half	Production at Double Time	Straight-Time Production	Production at Time and One Half	Production at Double Time
Jan. '57	0 12,500	−1.294	−2.588	−M	−M	−M	−M	−M	−M	−M	−M	−M	−M	−M	−M	−M	−M	−M
Feb. '57	−0.361 7500	−1.677	−2.992	0	−1.294	−2.588	−M	−M	−M	−M	−M	−M	−M	−M	−M	−M	−M	−M
Mar. '57	−0.728 960	−2.066	−3.423	−0.361 11,600	−1.677	−2.992	0 4940	−1.294	−2.588	−M	−M	−M	−M	−M	−M	−M	−M	−M
Apr. '57	−1.101	−2.462	−3.841	−0.728	−2.066	−3.423	−0.361 19,006	−1.677	−2.992	0 3494	−1.294	−2.588	−M	−M	−M	−M	−M	−M
May '57	−1.480	−2.864	−4.249	−1.101	−2.462	−3.841	−0.728	−2.066	−3.423	−0.361 16,452	−1.677	−2.992	0 1048	−1.294	−2.588	−M	−M	−M
June '57	−1.866	−3.273	−4.682	−1.480	−2.864	−4.249	−1.101	−2.462	−3.841	−0.728	−2.066	−3.423	−0.361 20,000	−1.677	−2.992	0 18,933	−1.294	−2.588
July '57	−2.258	−3.689	−5.121	−1.866	−3.273	−4.682	−1.480	−2.864	−4.249	−1.101	−2.462	−3.841	−0.728 1245	−2.066	−3.423	−0.361	−1.677	−2.992
Aug. '57	−2.656	−4.112	−5.567	−2.258	−3.689	−5.121	−1.866	−3.273	−4.682	−1.480	−2.864	−4.249	−1.101	−2.462	−3.841	−0.728	−2.066	−3.423
Sept. '57	−3.061	−4.542	−6.021	−2.656	−4.112	−5.567	−2.258	−3.689	−5.121	−1.866	−3.273	−4.682	−1.480	−2.864	−4.249	−1.101	−2.462	−3.841
Oct. '57	−3.473	−4.979	−6.482	−3.061	−4.542	−6.021	−2.656	−4.112	−5.567	−2.258	−3.689	−5.121	−1.866	−3.273	−4.682	−1.480	−2.864	−4.249
Nov. '57	−3.892	−5.423	−6.951	−3.473	−4.979	−6.482	−3.061	−4.542	−6.021	−2.656	−4.112	−5.567	−2.258	−3.689	−5.121	−1.866	−3.273	−4.682
Dec. '57	−4.318	−5.874	−7.428	−3.892	−5.423	−6.951	−3.473	−4.979	−6.482	−3.061	−4.542	−6.021	−2.656	−4.112	−5.567	−2.258	−3.689	−5.121
Dummy	0	0 9069	0 3819	0	0 5170	0 2304	0	0 11,699	0 5706	0	0 8781	0 3797	0	0 9728	0 4096	0	0 9493	0 4746
Total	20,960	9069	3819	11,600	5170	2304	23,946	11,699	5706	19,946	8781	3797	22,293	9728	4096	18,933	9493	4746

Production Month / Sales Month	July '57			Aug. '57			Sept. '57			Oct. '57			Nov. '57			Dec. '57			Total
	Straight-Time Production	Production at Time and One Half	Production at Double Time	Straight-Time Production	Production at Time and One Half	Production at Double Time	Straight-Time Production	Production at Time and One Half	Production at Double Time	Straight-Time Production	Production at Time and One Half	Production at Double Time	Straight-Time Production	Production at Time and One Half	Production at Double Time	Straight-Time Production	Production at Time and One Half	Production at Double Time	
Jan. '57	−M	−M	−M	−M	−M	−M	−M	−M	−M	−M	−M	−M	−M	−M	−M	−M	−M	−M	12,500
Feb. '57	−M	−M	−M	−M	−M	−M	−M	−M	−M	−M	−M	−M	−M	−M	−M	−M	−M	−M	7,500
Mar. '57	−M	−M	−M	−M	−M	−M	−M	−M	−M	−M	−M	−M	−M	−M	−M	−M	−M	−M	17,500
Apr. '57	−M	−M	−M	−M	−M	−M	−M	−M	−M	−M	−M	−M	−M	−M	−M	−M	−M	−M	22,500
May '57	−M	−M	−M	−M	−M	−M	−M	−M	−M	−M	−M	−M	−M	−M	−M	−M	−M	−M	17,500
June '57	−M	−M	−M	−M	−M	−M	−M	−M	−M	−M	−M	−M	−M	−M	−M	−M	−M	−M	20,000
July '57	0 4822	−1.294	−2.588	−M	−M	−M	−M	−M	−M	−M	−M	−M	−M	−M	−M	−M	−M	−M	25,000
Aug. '57	−0.361 14,805	−1.677	−2.992	0 12,695	−1.294	−2.588	−M	−M	−M	−M	−M	−M	−M	−M	−M	−M	−M	−M	27,500
Sept. '57	−0.728	−2.066	−3.423	−0.361 11,598	−1.677	−2.992	0 20,902	−1.294	−2.588	−M	−M	−M	−M	−M	−M	−M	−M	−M	32,500
Oct. '57	−1.101	−2.462	−3.841	−0.728	−2.066	−3.423	−0.361 6031	−1.677	−2.992	0 21,872	−1.294 2097	−2.588	−M	−M	−M	−M	−M	−M	30,000
Nov. '57	−1.480	−2.864	−4.249	−1.101	−2.462	−3.841	−0.728	−2.066	−3.423	−0.361 101	−1.677	−2.992	0 14,933	−1.294 7466	−2.588	−M	−M	−M	22,500
Dec. '57	−1.866	−3.273	−4.682	−1.480	−2.864	−4.249	−1.101	−2.462	−3.841	−0.728	−2.066	−3.423	−0.361	−1.677	−2.992	0 14,267	−1.294 733	−2.588	15,000
Dummy	0	0 8461	0 3562	0	0 11,592	0 4416	0	0 12,077	0 6746	0	0 7211	0 3818	0	0	0 2986	0	0 5143	0 3253	147,673
Total	19,627	8461	3562	24,293	11,592	4416	26,933	12,077	6746	21,973	9308	3818	14,933	7466	2986	14,267	5876	3253	397,673

Fig. 116. Distribution Matrix—Optimum Production Plan

Note that the rim conditions have been balanced with the dummy row (row 13) which represents fictitious demand for the product. In the real physical situation, this represents unutilized producing capacity. Note also that the cost factors for about half of the matrix are $-M$. Since back orders are not considered practical in this problem, the $-M$ cost (defined as so large that it dominates all else in the problem) accomplishes this restriction. If management allowed back orders, then a suitable cost factor could be used. However, such a cost would be difficult if not impossible to obtain.

Optimum Solution. The production planning problem can now be solved by any of the distribution methods. Vogel's Approximation Method (VAM) and subsequent improvement with the modified-distribution method yielded the answer in several steps[44] by hand. The problem can also be solved by automatic computers. However, the cost of machine computation over hand computation for a problem of this size might be difficult to justify. The optimum (lowest-cost) solution to the distribution matrix is shown in Figure 116 and summarized in Figure 117.

Figure 118 shows a cost summary of the optimum solution.

A quick analysis of this solution indicates that it is a totally practical solution as it stands. If it were not, however, phase II would proceed to modify the lowest-cost solution to one that would be compatible with the various management policies.

The second phase in production planning can modify the lowest-cost solution of phase I by analysis of the water-square evaluations. If a modification must be made, then the water-square evaluations will show how the modification can be accomplished at the lowest possible increase in costs.

Two points about the problem should be borne in mind. First, this problem assumes a zero lead time from manufacturing to consumer sales. Though this is seldom if ever the real case, a suitable lead time can easily be included in the problem formulation. Second, the inventory charges are cumulative and calculated monthly for a full month's storage in inventory. In an actual situation this

[44] This problem required the VAM plus six steps with the MODI method for solution. This required 10 hours. However, I believed that the solution could be accomplished in fewer steps and a shorter time period. This was verified by re-solving the problem requiring the VAM + two steps with the MODI method. This was accomplished in approximately 3 hours. However, this probably reflects bias due to prior knowledge of the solution. This same problem required only 15 minutes to solve with the IBM 650 computer.

January	Produce 20,960 units	Sell 12,500 in January
		Sell 7,500 in February
		Sell 960 in March
February	Produce 11,600 units	Sell 11,600 in March
March	Produce 23,946 units	Sell 4,940 in March
		Sell 19,006 in April
April	Produce 19,946 units	Sell 3,494 in April
		Sell 16,452 in May
May	Produce 22,293 units	Sell 1,048 in May
		Sell 20,000 in June
		Sell 1,245 in July
June	Produce 18,933 units	Sell 18,933 in July
July	Produce 19,627 units	Sell 4,822 in July
		Sell 14,805 in August
August	Produce 24,293 units	Sell 12,695 in August
		Sell 11,598 in September
September	Produce 26,933 units	Sell 20,902 in September
		Sell 6,031 in October
October	Produce 21,973 units	Sell 21,872 in October
		Sell 101 in November
	*Produce 2,097	Sell 2,097 in October
November	Produce 14,933 units	Sell 14,933 in November
	*Produce 7,466	Sell 7,466 in November
December	Produce 14,267 units	Sell 14,267 in December
	*Produce 733	Sell 733 in December

*At overtime.

Fig. 117. Final Optimum Solution

may vary somewhat and could conceivably reduce the inventory charges.

It can be seen from the final optimum solution (Fig. 117) that a FIFO (first-in-first-out) inventory system is in effect. This is partly due to the compound inventory charges that were used. In general a FIFO inventory system will be more economical than a LIFO (last-in-first-out) system when inventory charges are compounded.

Mr. G. T. Bishop[45] has presented an interesting modification of

[45] G. T. Bishop, "On a Problem of Production Scheduling," *Journal of the Operations Research Society of America,* V. 5, No. 1, February 1957, pp. 97–103.

Production Plan Cost Summary

Manufacturing Costs		
Direct material costs	$2,500,000.00	
250,000 units @ $10.00		
Direct labor costs		
250,000 units @ 1.5 man-hours per unit		
@ $1.725 per hour	646,875.00	
Manufacturing burden @ 200% direct labor	1,293,750.00	
Total maunfacturing costs		$4,440,625.00
Additional Costs		
Overtime premiums	$ 13,323.02	
Inventory charges	38,632.29	
Floor-space charges	8,478.34	
Total additional costs		$ 60,433.65
Total costs and charges		$4,501,058.65
Average unit cost = $18.005		

Fig. 118. Final Solution—Cost Summary

the solution method when inventory costs are not compounded. The costs are then such that any change within the body of the matrix, after an initial solution is made, will yield no increase or decrease in costs, unless a change occurs in the dummy row (or column). This fact then permits rather easy and rapid solution of the problem. However, this method would not apply too well in the preceding problem, even if the costs were not compounded.

ANOTHER PROBLEM

Another problem, somewhat similar to the preceding one, was solved. This problem better illustrates the two phases of the analysis. The distribution matrix for this problem is shown in Figure 119. It can be seen that the inventory costs are considerably higher than in the preceding problem and that a two-month lead time has been included. This lead time means that production must precede sales by two months. The optimum (lowest-cost) solution is shown in Figure 120.

Here the solution implies layoffs in November, March, September, and October, whereas it calls for overtime in February, June, July, and August. This type of labor fluctuation would probably not be consistent with the established policies; therefore, the optimum solution of phase I must be modified to fit the established policies and any other intangible considerations. This is probably more indicative of the solution that will result from a real problem.

PRODUCTION PLANNING—SEVERAL PRODUCTS

In the preceding problem, the production planning was accomplished for only one product. Actually a better over-all production plan could result if the problem included all the various products manufactured by this organization. This would not present an unsolvable situation.

Problems involving two or more products can be handled in several ways. One approach, suggested by Mr. Bowman,[46] is to handle the production and sales demand data in terms of man-hours or some type of equivalent units. This will, in effect, add 12 rows to the matrix for every product. Though this will greatly increase the size of the matrix array, it still remains a solvable problem, at least by high-speed calculating equipment.

Another approach is to consider the problem as a multidimensional distribution problem amendable to solution by the approximation method presented in Chapter 2. Here the solution would be best obtained by high-speed calculating equipment. This multidimensional approach permits many other possible extensions of the basic production planning problem.

In either case, the cost, capacity, and demand figures will probably be in terms of equivalent units or man-hours. This means that the sales demands must be converted to man-hours, and the manufacturing and inventory costs must be in terms of cost per unit man-hour.

Of course, as a problem becomes more complex, the number of calculations and the time and effort in solution increase. Likewise, the analysis of phase II becomes increasingly more complex.

SUMMARY

This approach to manufacturing planning offers a more comprehensive analysis than is usually considered. Intangible factors can

[46] Bowman, *op. cit.*, pp. 101–102.

Production Month / Sales Month	Nov. '56			Dec. '56			Jan. '57			Feb. '57			Mar. '57			Apr. '57		
	Straight-Time Production	Production at Time and One Half	Production at Double Time	Straight-Time Production	Production at Time and One Half	Production at Double Time	Straight-Time Production	Production at Time and One Half	Production at Double Time	Straight-Time Production	Production at Time and One Half	Production at Double Time	Straight-Time Production	Production at Time and One Half	Production at Double Time	Straight-Time Production	Production at Time and One Half	Production at Double Time
Jan. '57	0	−1.570	−3.142	−M	−M	−M	−M	−M	−M	−M	−M	−M	−M	−M	−M	−M	−M	−M
Feb. '57	−0.691	−2.288	−3.886	0	−1.570	−3.142	−M	−M	−M	−M	−M	−M	−M	−M	−M	−M	−M	−M
Mar. '57	−1.394	−3.018	−4.642	−0.691	−2.288	−3.886	0	−1.570	−3.142	−M	−M	−M	−M	−M	−M	−M	−M	−M
Apr. '57	−2.109	−3.760	−5.411	−1.394	−3.018	−4.642	−0.691	−2.288	−3.886	0	−1.570	−3.142	−M	−M	−M	−M	−M	−M
May '57	−2.836	−4.514	−6.193	−2.109	−3.760	−5.411	−1.394	−3.018	−4.642	−0.691	−2.288	−3.886	0	−1.570	−3.142	−M	−M	−M
June '57	−3.575	−5.281	−6.988	−2.836	−4.514	−6.193	−2.109	−3.760	−5.411	−1.394	−3.018	−4.642	−0.691	−2.288	−3.886	0	−1.570	−3.142
July '57	−4.326	−6.060	−7.796	−3.575	−5.281	−6.988	−2.836	−4.514	−6.193	−2.109	−3.760	−5.411	−1.394	−3.018	−4.642	−0.691	−2.288	−3.886
Aug. '57	−5.089	−6.852	−8.617	−4.326	−6.060	−7.796	−3.575	−5.281	−6.988	−2.836	−4.514	−6.193	−2.109	−3.760	−5.411	−1.394	−3.018	−4.642
Sept. '57	−5.865	−7.658	−9.452	−5.089	−6.852	−8.617	−4.326	−6.060	−7.796	−3.575	−5.281	−6.988	−2.836	−4.514	−6.193	−2.109	−3.760	−5.411
Oct. '57	−6.654	−8.477	−10.301	−5.865	−7.658	−9.452	−5.089	−6.852	−8.617	−4.326	−6.060	−7.796	−3.575	−5.281	−6.988	−2.836	−4.514	−6.193
Nov. '57	−7.456	−9.310	−11.164	−6.654	−8.477	−10.301	−5.865	−7.658	−9.452	−5.089	−6.852	−8.617	−4.326	−6.060	−7.796	−3.575	−5.281	−6.988
Dec. '57	−8.272	−10.157	−12.041	−7.456	−9.310	−11.164	−6.654	−8.477	−10.301	−5.865	−7.658	−9.452	−5.089	−6.852	−8.617	−4.326	−6.060	−7.796
Dummy	0	0	0	0	0	0	0	0	0	0	0	0	0	0	0	0	0	0
Total	16,780	7400	3200	12,087	6188	3173	21,627	9373	3947	11,933	5376	2389	24,280	11,863	5787	21,627	9373	3947

Sales Month \ Production Month	May '57			June '57			July '57			Aug. '57			Sept. '57			Oct. '57			Total
	Straight-Time Production	Production at Time and One Half	Production at Double Time	Straight-Time Production	Production at Time and One Half	Production at Double Time	Straight-Time Production	Production at Time and One Half	Production at Double Time	Straight-Time Production	Production at Time and One Half	Production at Double Time	Straight-Time Production	Production at Time and One Half	Production at Double Time	Straight-Time Production	Production at Time and One Half	Production at Double Time	
Jan. '57	−M	−M	−M	−M	−M	−M	−M	−M	−M	−M	−M	−M	−M	−M	−M	−M	−M	−M	12,500
Feb. '57	−M	−M	−M	−M	−M	−M	−M	−M	−M	−M	−M	−M	−M	−M	−M	−M	−M	−M	7,500
Mar. '57	−M	−M	−M	−M	−M	−M	−M	−M	−M	−M	−M	−M	−M	−M	−M	−M	−M	−M	17,500
Apr. '57	−M	−M	−M	−M	−M	−M	−M	−M	−M	−M	−M	−M	−M	−M	−M	−M	−M	−M	22,500
May '57	−M	−M	−M	−M	−M	−M	−M	−M	−M	−M	−M	−M	−M	−M	−M	−M	−M	−M	17,500
June '57	−M	−M	−M	−M	−M	−M	−M	−M	−M	−M	−M	−M	−M	−M	−M	−M	−M	−M	20,000
July '57	0	−1.570	−3.142	−M	−M	−M	−M	−M	−M	−M	−M	−M	−M	−M	−M	−M	−M	−M	25,000
Aug. '57	−0.691	−2.288	−3.886	0	−1.570	−3.142	−M	−M	−M	−M	−M	−M	−M	−M	−M	−M	−M	−M	27,500
Sept. '57	−1.394	−3.018	−4.642	−0.691	−2.288	−3.886	0	−1.570	−3.142	−M	−M	−M	−M	−M	−M	−M	−M	−M	32,500
Oct. '57	−2.109	−3.760	−5.411	−1.394	−3.018	−4.642	−0.691	−2.288	−3.886	0	−1.570	−3.142	−M	−M	−M	−M	−M	−M	30,000
Nov. '57	−2.836	−4.514	−6.193	−2.109	−3.760	−5.411	−1.394	−3.018	−4.642	−0.691	−2.288	−3.886	0	−1.570	−3.142	−M	−M	−M	22,500
Dec. '57	−3.575	−5.281	−6.988	−2.836	−4.514	−6.193	−2.109	−3.760	−5.411	−1.394	−3.018	−4.642	−0.691	−2.288	−3.886	0	−1.570	−3.142	15,000
Dummy	0	0	0	0	0	0	0	0	0	0	0	0	0	0	0	0	0	0	150,586
Total	21,627	9373	3947	19,433	9920	4960	19,127	8259	3477	24,127	11,536	4395	26,933	12,096	6720	21,473	9100	3733	400,586

Fig. 119. Production Plan—Matrix Array

Sales Month \ Production Month	Nov. '56			Dec. '56			Jan. '57			Feb. '57			Mar. '57			Apr. '57		
	Straight-Time Production	Production at Time and One Half	Production at Double Time	Straight-Time Production	Production at Time and One Half	Production at Double Time	Straight-Time Production	Production at Time and One Half	Production at Double Time	Straight-Time Production	Production at Time and One Half	Production at Double Time	Straight-Time Production	Production at Time and One Half	Production at Double Time	Straight-Time Production	Production at Time and One Half	Production at Double Time
Jan. '57	0 12,500	−1.570	−3.142	−M	−M	−M	−M	−M	−M	−M	−M	−M	−M	−M	−M	−M	−M	−M
Feb. '57	−0.691	−2.288	−3.886	0 7500	−1.570	−3.142	−M	−M	−M	−M	−M	−M	−M	−M	−M	−M	−M	−M
Mar. '57	−1.394	−3.018	−4.642	−0.691 4587	−2.288	−3.886	0 12,913	−1.570	−3.142	−M	−M	−M	−M	−M	−M	−M	−M	−M
Apr. '57	−2.109	−3.760	−5.411	−1.394	−3.018	−4.642	−0.691 8714	−2.288	−3.886	0 11,933	−1.570 1853	−3.142	−M	−M	−M	−M	−M	−M
May '57	−2.836	−4.514	−6.193	−2.109	−3.760	−5.411	−1.394	−3.018	−4.642	−0.691	−2.288	−3.886	0 17,500	−1.570	−3.142	−M	−M	−M
June '57	−3.575	−5.281	−6.988	−2.836	−4.514	−6.193	−2.109	−3.760	−5.411	−1.394	−3.018	−4.642	−0.691 5007	−2.288	−3.886	0 14,933	−1.570	−3.142
July '57	−4.326	−6.060	−7.796	−3.575	−5.281	−6.988	−2.836	−4.514	−6.193	−2.109	−3.760	−5.411	−1.394	−3.018	−4.642	−0.691 6634	−2.288	−3.886
Aug. '57	−5.089	−6.852	−8.617	−4.326	−6.060	−7.796	−3.575	−5.281	−6.988	−2.836	−4.514	−6.193	−2.109	−3.760	−5.411	−1.394	−3.018	−4.642
Sept. '57	−5.865	−7.658	−9.452	−5.089	−6.852	−8.617	−4.326	−6.060	−7.796	−3.575	−5.281	−6.988	−2.836	−4.514	−6.193	−2.109	−3.760	−5.411
Oct. '57	−6.654	−8.477	−10.301	−5.865	−7.658	−9.452	−5.089	−6.852	−8.617	−4.326	−6.060	−7.796	−3.575	−5.281	−6.988	−2.836	−4.514	−6.193
Nov. '57	−7.456	−9.310	−11.164	−6.654	−8.477	−10.301	−5.865	−7.658	−9.452	−5.089	−6.852	−8.617	−4.326	−6.060	−7.796	−3.575	−5.281	−6.988
Dec. '57	−8.272	−10.157	−12.041	−7.456	−9.310	−11.164	−6.654	−8.477	−10.301	−5.865	−7.658	−9.452	−5.089	−6.852	−8.617	−4.326	−6.060	−7.796
Dummy	0 4280	0 7400	0 3200	0	0 6188	0 3173	0	0 9373	0 3947	0	0 3523	0 2389	0 1773	0 11,863	0 5787	0	0 9373	0 3947
Total	16,780	7400	3200	12,087	6188	3173	21,627	9373	3947	11,933	5376	2389	24,280	11,863	5787	21,627	9373	3947

Production Month / Sales Month	May '57			June '57			July '57			Aug. '57			Sept. '57			Oct. '57			Total
	Straight-Time Production	Production at Time and One Half	Production at Double Time	Straight-Time Production	Production at Time and One Half	Production at Double Time	Straight-Time Production	Production at Time and One Half	Production at Double Time	Straight-Time Production	Production at Time and One Half	Production at Double Time	Straight-Time Production	Production at Time and One Half	Production at Double Time	Straight-Time Production	Production at Time and One Half	Production at Double Time	
Jan. '57	−M	−M	−M	−M	−M	−M	−M	−M	−M	−M	−M	−M	−M	−M	−M	−M	−M	−M	12,500
Feb. '57	−M	−M	−M	−M	−M	−M	−M	−M	−M	−M	−M	−M	−M	−M	−M	−M	−M	−M	7,500
Mar. '57	−M	−M	−M	−M	−M	−M	−M	−M	−M	−M	−M	−M	−M	−M	−M	−M	−M	−M	17,500
Apr. '57	−M	−M	−M	−M	−M	−M	−M	−M	−M	−M	−M	−M	−M	−M	−M	−M	−M	−M	22,500
May '57	−M	−M	−M	−M	−M	−M	−M	−M	−M	−M	−M	−M	−M	−M	−M	−M	−M	−M	17,500
June '57	−M	−M	−M	−M	−M	−M	−M	−M	−M	−M	−M	−M	−M	−M	−M	−M	−M	−M	20,000
July '57	0 18,366	−1.570	−3.142	−M	−M	−M	−M	−M	−M	−M	−M	−M	−M	−M	−M	−M	−M	−M	25,000
Aug. '57	−0.691 3261	−2.288	−3.886	0 14,319	−1.570 9920	−3.142	−M	−M	−M	−M	−M	−M	−M	−M	−M	−M	−M	−M	27,500
Sept. '57	−1.394	−3.018	−4.642	−0.691 5114	−2.288	−3.886	0 19,127	−1.570 8259	−3.142	−M	−M	−M	−M	−M	−M	−M	−M	−M	32,500
Oct. '57	−2.109	−3.760	−5.411	−1.394	−3.018	−4.642	−0.691	−2.288	−3.886	0 24,127	−1.570 5873	−3.142	−M	−M	−M	−M	−M	−M	30,000
Nov. '57	−2.836	−4.514	−6.193	−2.109	−3.760	−5.411	−1.394	−3.018	−4.642	−0.691	−2.288	−3.886	0 22,500	−1.570	−3.142	−M	−M	−M	22,500
Dec. '57	−3.575	−5.281	−6.988	−2.836	−4.514	−6.193	−2.109	−3.760	−5.411	−1.394	−3.018	−4.642	−0.691	−2.288	−3.886	0 15,000	−1.570	−3.142	15,000
Dummy	0	0 9373	0 3947	0	0	0 4960	0	0	0 3477	0	0 5663	0 4395	0 4433	0 12,096	0 6720	0 6473	0 9100	0 3733	150,586
Total	21,627	9373	3947	19,433	9920	4960	19,127	8259	3477	24,127	11,536	4395	26,933	12,096	6720	21,473	9100	3733	400,586

Fig. 120. Production Plan—Optimum Solution

be somewhat more objectively reviewed in terms of their effects upon the various costs.

However, it is necessary here to offer a word or two of caution. This type of solution does not and cannot include costs associated with labor fluctuations and turnover and other such nonlinear items (costs that do not vary directly with the production quantities). Nor can it include costs associated with less than full budgeted utilization of equipment and facilities, since this affects the manufacturing burden rate, and hence burden costs. Then too, the production plan is only as good as the sales forecast. This means that, no matter how well a production plan is developed, it is poor if it is based on an ill-conceived sales forecast.

In a real situation, the greatest difficulty is not in obtaining the numerical solution but in obtaining meaningful costs, capacities, and requirements. If desired, alternative production plans might be based on some established upper and lower limits of the sales forecast. Comparison of these alternative plans for the upper limit, the mean, and the lower limit of the sales forecast will provide management with a guide as to the flexibility of the production plan with a variable sales forecast. This additional information can be very useful in such situations. Some work is presently being conducted to develop methods for solving distribution problems where the quantities (rim conditions) are expressed as a probability distribution about some average value. However, this is still in the early stages of development.

The problem can be expanded to include planning for the desired inventories period by period. Here the problem matrix takes on more rows or columns as the various inventories are included. In some situations this would be a more desirable formulation of the problem.

The production planning may be accomplished on a continuous basis, either monthly or quarterly, for the next twelve-month period. This type of continuous planning means that a twelve-month plan is always available. While this requires more work, it means that more and better information is available to management. A once-per-year planning cannot include changes in sales demand from the original forecast. Continuous planning can successfully accomplish such changes. Less risk of suboptimization (optimizing one year's plan at a sacrifice in the next year's plan) would result in continuous planning.

The production planning problem may be expanded to include several products. It is necessary, in considering such problems, to express the production and sales in some common unit such as man-hours or equivalent units or in terms of one hour's production as suggested by Mr. Bowman.[47] Though this would increase the size (number of columns) of the distribution matrix, it still remains a solvable problem. However, if one considers this as a multidimensional type of problem, then the approximation method discussed in Chapter 2 can be applied to solve the problem. The multidimensional approach permits many more possible extensions to the basic production planning problem. In the problem presented here, the most economic manufacturing plan for all products can be simultaneously developed by this approach. This then will reduce the danger of suboptimization inherent in the problem presented here.

The application of mathematical programming to production planning is significant in that it was the first application to a dynamic problem. It was held for a time that mathematical programming was a tool limited to static analysis. This, however, is not the case. A useful extension of this application might be in the distribution of products from various sources to various locations when the available supply and the demand fluctuate widely period to period. A better distribution can result from considering the total problem rather than one period at a time. The danger of suboptimization (optimizing one problem at a sacrifice to another problem) is materially reduced if the entire problem can be handled in the same analysis.

It was mentioned previously that automatic high-speed computers might be used for this type of problem. It is entirely feasible that all the calculations in the example problem could be programmed so that a computer would do all the work, beginning with the initial sales demand and the basic problem data, and ending with the optimum distribution matrix.

[47] *Ibid.*

8.

Stock Slitting

Stock slitting presents a problem that can be successfully solved via mathematical programming. The term stock slitting refers here to the process whereby narrow rolls or coils of paper, Cellophane, foil, textiles, metal, or other materials are cut from wider rolls. This is accomplished either by slicing the roll much like bread is sliced, or unwinding the roll, passing it through a set of knives, and then rewinding it. The machine that accomplishes this slitting has a number of knives which can be set in a number of positions. Hence a number of various widths can be cut from a roll at any one time.

The problem in stock slitting arises from the fact that seldom do the orders for coils of the various slit widths provide for full utilization of the entire available width of the initial roll. Hence a portion of the initial roll (which is usually called trim) is either scraped as too narrow for use or inventoried for some future use when it will again pass through the slitting operation. In the first case, the trim material is wasted. In the latter case, additional costs are incurred in inventory, and, with some materials, additional trim losses are incurred. Mathematical programming permits the stock slitting operation to be accomplished in such a manner that the orders for the various widths of stock are filled with an absolute minimum trim loss. At the same time, the mathematical analysis can control or minimize overproduction of the various slit coils, thus minimizing the inventory problem. The discussion here will consider slitting exactly to meet the requirements, and hence eliminating this inventory problem.

THE GENERAL PROBLEM ANALYSIS

The mathematical approach to the stock slitting problem involves two phases. The initial phase in the analysis is to determine all the possible settings of the slitter knives (subject to criteria as outlined below). Each setting of the knives produces a certain combination of slit coils of various widths plus some trim loss. It is necessary to determine these combinations in light of:

1. The various slit widths that are required from a particular material specification, weight, or gage.
2. The usable width of the coil prior to slitting.
3. The maximum number of cuts permitted at any one time.

These, of course, determine to a large degree the total number of combinations possible. This initial phase provides the matrix for the mathematical programming analysis of the problem.

The second phase of the problem is to determine how many coils to cut into the various combinations to meet the orders for the various slit widths with the minimum trim loss. This is further explained in the following problem.

A PROBLEM

The problem presented here is adapted from an actual steel stock slitting problem. However, the problem analysis would be very similar for other materials. At this point it may be well to define several terms which will be used.

Initial coils—Coils as purchased or those coils prior to the slitting operation.

Slit coils—Coils of widths somewhat narrower than the initial coils; those coils produced by the slitting operation.

Combination—A number of slit coil widths plus trim loss produced with one setting of the slitter knives.

In slitting most metallic materials, it is impossible to utilize the entire width of an initial coil, owing to the irregularities in the edges of the coils. These irregularities in the edge of the coil can break a cutter knife if it runs off the edge or can result in slit coils with irregular edges which can cause a variety of problems in the subsequent processing of the material. This means that a portion of the coil is lost in unavoidable trim, and that a somewhat narrower portion of the initial coil width is actually available to be made into slit coils. Figure 121 illustrates this situation.

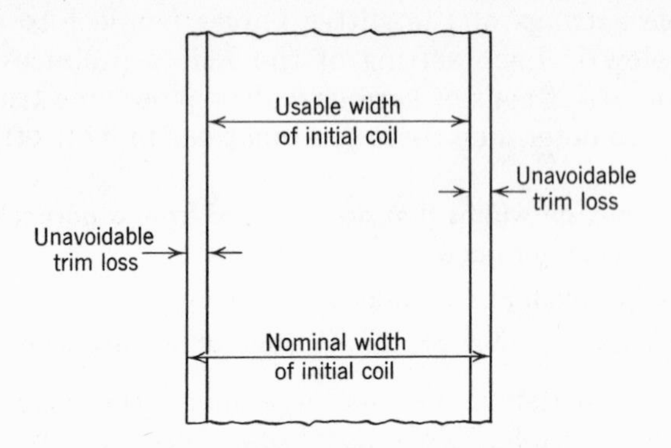

Fig. 121. Trim Loss in the Initial Coil

The unavoidable trim loss is usually established by experience and is generally ¼ inch on each edge or ½ inch total. This means that an initial coil 36 inches wide provides 35½ inches of width available for making into slit coils.

The initial phase of the mathematical analysis requires the development of cutting combinations. These combinations, the variables in the subsequent linear programming analysis, can be developed either by hand or via suitable computing equipment. In either case, however, some limitations must be placed on these combinations. These are:

W—The usable width of the initial coil; no combination can exceed this total width.

N—The maximum number of coils that can be cut at any one time. This may be determined by the power capacity of the slitting machine or the number of knives or knife settings available.

n—The number of slit widths to be cut from a given specification of material.

These limitations, however, permit combinations that may only utilize a small portion of the usable width of the initial coil. This would require the remaining portions of the initial coil to be inventoried and subsequently reprocessed through the slitting operation. Generally this reprocessing (or multiple-pass slitting as it is called) is avoided whenever possible, because, first, some additional unavoidable trim loss is required in each subsequent pass through the slitter, and, second, the effective utilization of the slitting machine is considerably reduced. To eliminate combinations resulting in multiple passes, an additional limitation can be placed on the combinations. This limitation is

t—The maximum permissible trim loss. No acceptable combination can result in a trim loss $> t$.

Generally this maximum permissible trim loss t will be smaller than the narrowest slit coil width, since a larger trim loss could be reprocessed into a slit coil.

The total possible number of combinations, of course, depends upon all four of the above parameters. However, the maximum permissible trim loss is the only parameter that can have the most latitude. Certainly to limit t to a very small amount may well overrestrict the problem, yielding the entire analysis less than truly optimum. On the other hand, if t is too large, the number of acceptable combinations may be so numerous that the resulting mathematical programming analysis would be excessive even for computing equipment.

The Data. Consider a steel stock slitting problem with data as follows:

Material: Hot-rolled steel, purchased in nominally 5000-pound coils. (The actual coils weigh between 3000 and 6000 pounds.)

Gage: 0.078 inch thick by 28⁹⁄₁₆ inches wide.

This material results in the following values for the four parameters to determine the combinations:

$W = 28\frac{1}{4}$ inches, usable width of the coil (0.3125 inch unavoidable trim loss)

$N = 11$, maximum number of slit widths in any one combination

$n = 6$, the number of slit widths cut from this material
$t = 0.728$ maximum permissible trim loss for any combination (This value was arbitrarily selected for t)

The slit widths and monthly requirements are as follows:

Slit Width, inches	Requirements, pounds
9⅞	68,000
9⅜	454,000
8½	44,000
4 1/16	24,500
3 47/64	44,500
2 7/32	21,000

The Analysis. The initial phase in the analysis is the development of all the acceptable combinations. Forty-seven acceptable combinations result in this problem and are as shown in Figure 122.

These combinations can be developed in several man-hours by hand, or they can be developed by an IBM 650 computer in approximately 6 minutes.[48] As shown in Figure 122, each combination becomes a variable in the simplex matrix, and each slit width represents an equation. The trim loss, in inches, becomes the objective function. Hence the mathematical programming analysis of this problem must solve a 6×53 system (6 equations, 47 combinations, plus the 6×6 identity of artificial variables).

The second phase in the problem analysis, namely the mathematical programming, can proceed then to determine the number of coils of the various combinations necessary to meet the requirements with minimum trim loss. Before this can be done, however, the requirements must be modified to the number of coils of the various slit widths. This is necessary since each combination is expressed in terms of numbers of coils. For example, in each coil cut into combinations P_{28}, two coils 8½ inches wide and three coils 3 47/64 inches wide are produced. Hence the problem analysis is most easily affected by dealing with everything in terms of number of coils.

Assuming 5000-pound coils and determining the weight per coil

[48] The IBM 650 computer program to develop the combinations for this and any other slitting problem can be obtained from me. The program will generate combinations for problems having up to 100 slit widths. A similar program is available for the IBM 704 computer.

Trim Loss			0	.375	.705	.0001	.328	.50	.50	.125	.1875	.234	.562	.187	.5157	.540	.125	.625	.313	.3594	.6875	.406	.0314	.3595	.6876	.203
Acceptable Combinations			P_1	P_2	P_3	P_4	P_5	P_6	P_7	P_8	P_9	P_{10}	P_{11}	P_{12}	P_{13}	P_{14}	P_{15}	P_{16}	P_{17}	P_{18}	P_{19}	P_{20}	P_{21}	P_{22}	P_{23}	P_{24}
SLIT WIDTHS	9⅞	x_1	2	2	2	2	2	1	1	1	1	1	1	1	1	1										
	9⅜	x_2						1	1	1							3	2	1	1	1	1	1	1	1	1
	8½	x_3	1					1			1								1	1	1					
	4 1/16	x_4		2	1	1			1			3	2	1					2	1		4	3	2	1	
	3 47/64	x_5			1		1				2	1	2	2	3					1	2			1	2	5
	2 7/32	x_6				2	2		2	4	1	1	1	3	3	8		4	1	1	1	1	3	3	3	

Trim Loss			.3127	.531	.531	.0468	.1565	.0937	.4218	.5315	.047	.157	.375	.485	.141	.469	.094	.422	.532	.047	.157	.375	.485	.703	.0002
Acceptable Combinations			P_{25}	P_{26}	P_{27}	P_{28}	P_{29}	P_{30}	P_{31}	P_{32}	P_{33}	P_{34}	P_{35}	P_{36}	P_{37}	P_{38}	P_{39}	P_{40}	P_{41}	P_{42}	P_{43}	P_{44}	P_{45}	P_{46}	P_{47}
SLIT WIDTHS	9⅞	x_1																							
	9⅜	x_2	1																						
	8½	x_3		3	2	2	2	1	1	1	1	1	1	1											
	4 1/16	x_4			1			3	2	2	1	1			6	5	4	3	3	2	2	1	1		
	3 47/64	x_5	3			3		2	3		3		4	1	1	2	2	3		3		4	1	5	4
	2 7/32	x_6	5	1	3		5			5	2	7	2	7			2	2	7	4	9	4	9	4	6

Fig. 122. Acceptable Combinations for a Stock Slitting Problem with the Parameters: $W = 28.250$, $N = 11$, $n = 6$, $t = 0.728$ inch

as a percentage of the width of the initial coil, the requirements become:

Slit Width, inches	Weight per Coil, pounds	Requirements Pounds	Requirements Coils
9⅞	1706.5	68,000	40
9⅜	1620	454,000	280
8½	1468.5	44,000	30
4$\frac{1}{16}$	702	24,500	35
3$\frac{47}{64}$	645.5	44,500	69
2$\frac{7}{32}$	383	21,000	55

These requirements have been rounded off to the nearest whole number of coils for convenience although this is not necessary. In fact, it will be shown later that this has a negligible effect upon the total problem. The requirements now complete the simplex array, and it is ready for solution.

The Solution. The optimum solution to the simplex array is as follows:[49]

Combination	No. of Coils
P_1	20.0
P_{15}	92.567
P_{28}	4.999
P_{37}	5.833
P_{24}	2.30
P_{47}	9.166

Total minimum trim loss 13.1379 inches.
(The avoidable trim from all coils totals 13.1379 inches.)

This optimum solution expressed in terms of the number of pounds of each combination, since steel slitting orders are usually issued on a poundage basis, is as follows:

Combination	No. of Coils	No. of pounds @ 5000 pounds per Coil
P_1	20.	100,000
P_{15}	92.567	463,000
P_{28}	4.999	25,000
P_{37}	5.833	29,167
P_{24}	2.3	11,500
P_{47}	9.166	46,000

[49] The solution was obtained in 8 iterations. This required 11 minutes on an IBM 650 computer.

This solution then is in the proper form for the stock slitting orders. The orders may be issued for the poundage as indicated above, or the weight may be rounded off to the nearest thousand pounds. Here is one situation where the results of the mathematical programming analysis are in exactly the same form as the present manner of operation in most industries.

This solution will yield the following amounts of the various slit widths.

Slit Width, inches	Poundage via Combination No.		
9⅞	69,150	P_1	
9⅜	455,916	P_{15}	
	3,984	P_{24}	459,900 lb. total
8½	29,750	P_1	
	14,880	P_{28}	44,630 lb. total
4¹⁄₁₆	24,748	P_{37}	
3⁴⁷⁄₆₄	9,805	P_{28}	
	3,790	P_{36}	
	7,844	P_{24}	
	24,058	P_{47}	45,497 lb. total
2⁷⁄₃₂	21,441	P_{47}	

Post-Solution Analysis. It can be readily seen that the solution meets the requirements as initially listed. This solution would result in the following approximate poundage if all the initial coils were exactly 28⁹⁄₁₆ inches wide:

665,366	Pounds resulting in slit coils
675,000	Actual pounds through the slitting machine
9,634	Total pounds of loss (avoidable and unavoidable trim)

This then results in a total trim loss of 1.427%.

If any or all of the initial coils were wider than 28⁹⁄₁₆ inches or heavier than 0.078 gage (one thousandth of an inch makes a noticeable difference), then, of course, the 5000-pound coils will result in higher trim loss and lower yield in slit coils. The following table illustrates the possible results with all initial coils at various widths.[50]

[50] This material can be received with initial coil widths varying between 28⁹⁄₁₆ to 29⁵⁄₁₆. This width is usually controlled within these limits by the steel rolling mill; hence the purchaser has no control over this width variation.

All coils this wide, inches	$28\frac{9}{16}$	$28\frac{15}{16}$	$29\frac{5}{16}$
Poundage resulting in slit coils	665,366	656,686	648,309
Total poundage	675,000	675,000	675,000
Total trim loss	9,634	18,314	26,691
Per cent trim loss	1.427	2.713	3.954

Several savings are indicated by this analysis. First is the savings in material. Most steel slitting operations range between 3 and 4 per cent total trim loss. It does not take a very large-volume slitting operation to realize a sizable savings in dollars with a reduction of only one quarter of 1 per cent in trim loss. Second, less material is handled and run through the slitting operation. This, too, can show a savings in dollars, although most of this is in terms of hidden costs. Third, the mathematical programming analysis tends to minimize the number of slitting-machine set-ups. In the preceding problem the requirements are met with only six settings of the cutter knives. In fact, the mathematical programming solution will never require more set-ups than the total number of slit widths.

SUMMARY

Stock slitting, whether of steel, fabric, tape, paper or any other materials, presents a problem readily solvable via mathematical programming. The two phases in the analysis are readily adaptable to high-speed computation equipment and for the first time permit a scientific analysis of the stock slitting problem.

In actual manufacturing operations, the combination generation would be accomplished rather infrequently. New combinations must be developed whenever a new size is added to a particular list. Otherwise, the same combinations remain valid for successive solutions with subsequent production requirements. It is of interest to note that, when the requirements are zero for a particular slit width, all combinations including that particular width may be dropped from the array, and the solution obtained with a smaller matrix. For example, if in the above problem the requirements were zero for the 8½-inch slit width, combinations P_1, P_6, P_9, P_{17}, P_{18}, P_{19}, and P_{26} through P_{36} could be dropped from the array, thus permitting the solution to be obtained by solving a 5×35 array (5 slit sizes and 30 combinations plus the 5×5 identity). The result would be similar if the 8½-inch slit width were dropped entirely.

This type of analysis also permits a tighter control on the slitting operation and a reduction in the lead-time requirements. Many manufacturers accomplish the stock slitting from three to four weeks ahead of subsequent manufacturing. The mathematical programming analysis, since it is independent of the time cycle, could be accomplished monthly, semimonthly, or even daily if necessary. Of course, the shorter the time period, the greater the risk of suboptimization. On the other hand, inventories can be reduced if the lead time is reduced.

The mathematical programming approach also offers an opportunity for analyzing various widths of initial coils. Certainly, as wider initial coils are used, the trim loss per cent will reduce. At present, most slitting operations specify the width of the initial coils as a multiple of a slit width having the highest requirements. This may not necessarily result in minimum trim loss. In the above problem the combination P_{15} (consisting of three cuts of the 9⅜-inch size) resulted in 0.125-inch trim loss. Since the 9⅜-inch size has by far the highest requirements, it would seem in order to investigate the results if the initial coils were 0.125-inch narrower. This can be rather easily accomplished via the above analysis. Similarly, one can investigate wider widths in attempting to justify a slitting machine for handling wider initial coils.[51]

In the problem presented here, a solution was obtained that produces exactly the necessary requirements. The problem can also be solved in several other ways. One formulation would permit overproduction if the equations were changed to requirements (the solution $\geq$ the requirements). Here one must place a suitable penalty on the slack variables representing overproduction. This penalty might reflect inventorying costs.

Another formulation is possible where another month's estimated or projected requirements are available. Here one can place upper and lower limits on the solution (one month's requirements $\leq$ the solution $\leq$ the total projected requirements). This then would yield a solution bounded on the bottom by one month's requirements and on the top by the total of one month's and the projected requirements. The simplex array for this analysis would

[51] These problems were considered in a research study, the results of which were reported in a paper, "The Application of Linear Programming to a Steel Stock Slitting Problem," by R. W. Metzger, for presentation at the ORSA meeting May 15, 1958.

contain twice as many rows (one restriction and one requirement per size), but would retain the same combinations.

The stock slitting problem is open to a very comprehensive scientific analysis via mathematical programming. Particularly so where high-speed computation facilities are available. This analysis of stock slitting has almost unlimited potential throughout industry. This problem is representative of a class of problems that require the two-phase analysis, namely: Determine possible combinations; then apply mathematical programming. Assembly-line balancing is a problem solvable in much the same way.

9. Material Handling Scheduling

Mathematical programming has been and can be applied to optimize nonautomated material handling. This particular application is interesting in that the mathematical programming portion of the problem is relatively small compared to the total problem, and the problem concerns itself with improving upon the existing system rather than changing the mode of handling or the plant layout. Nonautomated material handling refers to handling materials on skids or pallets or in cartons, drums, or tubs via fork-lift truck or other similar means. Almost any material handling other than that accomplished by conveyors can be approached with mathematical programming.

Two problems will be considered here. Before they are discussed, it might be well to describe the present state of the nonautomated material handling activity in industry. Most members of American management will concede that nonautomated material handling operates in the range of 40 per cent effectiveness. In terms of effectiveness and efficiency, this means of material handling is in the same state of development as the average factory job was at about the turn of the century. To illustrate—around 1900, before the widespread application of industrial engineering, the average factory worker received minimal job instructions, and a measure of a fair day's work was difficult, if not impossible, to obtain. Nowadays the worker's instructions are much more complete, and a measure of a fair day's work is available. By contrast, however, the worker in material handling today receives few, if any, instructions, and little or no attempt is made to schedule his activities to obtain optimum utilization of the man and his equipment. As a result, it is difficult and often outright impossible to develop and measure a fair day's work for people in a material handling assignment.

The major source of inefficiency in nonautomated material handling is in the "dead heading" or moving empty from one location to another. Though "dead heading" cannot necessarily be eliminated, it can be minimized with mathematical programming. This then permits optimum schedules to be prepared for the material handling activity, thereby realizing improved utilization of the equipment and manpower.

There are several important prerequisites or characteristics that must be met before any attempt can be made to improve the material handling activity. These are:

1. An adequate inventory and material control. This implies a well-ordered warehousing situation, with a designated place or area for everything, and everything in its place. This one characteristic was the major obstacle in a recent attempt to improve the material handling activity in an organization. It was possible to find the same material in several widely separated locations in the plant. Material was stored wherever an empty space was available. With such a situation existing, it is impossible to improve the material handling activity.

2. A measure of material handling time between the various locations. It is necessary to have a measure of handling time, including loading, unloading, moving loaded, and moving empty, among the various departments, warehouses, or internal shipping and receiving points in the plant, in order to develop the material handling schedules. Distance or cost can be used as a measure instead of time in some instances.

3. An indication of average material movements per day. The mathematical solution is based upon average material movements. The normal day-to-day variations can then be rather easily accommodated. The average moves per day can be simply a listing of origin, destination, and number of moves.

4. A daily indication of material requirements for the following day. Any type of schedule requires preplanning. This is the necessary preplanning information to allow optimum schedules to be prepared. In most industrial operations the work for the following day is known; hence most if not all the material requirements can be determined.

If these prerequisites can be obtained, then the analysis of a problem can proceed. This analysis takes the form of five phases, which are:

1. An initial survey to identify the various loading and unloading stations, and to determine the average number of material moves required per day.
2. Preparation of handling time data between every possible origin and destination, and time requirements for loading and unloading at the various locations.
3. Determination of the minimum "dead-heading" requirements via mathematical programming.
4. Development of round trips and subsequent schedules for the handling equipment.
5. Daily implementation and scheduling to realize the continued benefits in optimum utilization of the material handling equipment and personnel.

These phases and the mathematical programming approach can best be developed via a sample problem.

A PROBLEM[52]

This problem is relatively simple, although still typical, and will serve to illustrate this approach.

A factory consisting of five departments or work-load centers (*A, B, C, D, E*) desires to improve its material handling activity with the existing equipment and layout. The plant situation meets all of the required prerequisites.

Material handling is accomplished with a number of the same model fork-lift trucks. The same type container is used for all the items handled in this manufacturing operation. (It will be shown

---

[52] This problem is essentially the same as the problem presented in: R. W. Metzger, "In Fork Truck Operations . . . Linear Programming Can Cut Dead-Heading," *Flow Magazine,* May 1957, pp. 78–81+. I am indebted to the publishers of *Flow Magazine* for permission to present this material here. This presentation parallels to an extent the analysis presented by M. Klein and S. Milberg, "The Application of Linear Programming to Materials Handling," *Modern Materials Handling,* February 1955, pp. 80–84, and N. V. Reinfeld, *Tooling and Production,* April 1957.

later how the restriction on types of containers may be modified.) The containers are such that only one at a time may be handled by a truck.

The labor standards department has provided average time values for loading and unloading in the various departments, and for moving loaded and empty between them.

An initial survey of the material handling operation indicates the average material moves per day as follows:

Origin	Destination	Average No. of Moves per day
A	*C*	6.2
A	*D*	3.1
A	*E*	.8
B	*C*	1.3
B	*E*	3.7
C	*B*	3.1
C	*D*	5.3
D	*B*	1.8
D	*C*	3.6
D	*E*	2.9
E	*B*	7.4
E	*D*	1.0

Total average moves per day = 40.2

Note: This does not include many material movements that occur less frequently than once per day.

It is necessary to round off the average number of moves per day and to reorganize the survey data into a route table form. This is shown in Figure 123.

The average moves per day can be rather easily analyzed when shown in the route table form. Rounding off the number of moves and not including the less-than-once-per-day material movements does introduce a degree of error. However, this error can be overcome in the final analysis of the problem.

Actually the route table presents a part of the problem that cannot be improved upon unless the plant layout is changed or the mode of handling is modified—assuming, of course, that the shortest route is taken between any two points. However, the movements represented in the route table represent about one half of the total amount of time and effort in material handling. The lift trucks must, of necessity, spend a portion of the day moving between departments without a load. This part of the problem can be most easily seen if we consider the distribution of empty containers.

From \ To	B	C	D	E	Total
A		6	3	1	10
B		1		4	5
C	3		5		8
D	2	4		3	9
E	7		1		8
Total	12	11	9	8	40 \ 40

Fig. 123. Route Table—Average Number of Moves (Loaded) per day between Departments

In this problem department *A* sends out 12 containers of material per day to several departments. Unless an unlimited supply of containers is available at department *A,* it will soon run out of available containers. Similarly, unless the containers are automatically consumed in manufacturing, the empties will pile up at the various receiving departments. Therefore, the material handling activity must not only distribute the necessary container loads of material, but, since it is usually desirable to keep the system operative with a minimum of containers, it must also take care of the necessary distribution of empty containers. The problem then is to determine the most economical distribution of empty containers.

The distribution of empty containers can be easily accomplished if the route table (Fig. 123) is modified to form a distribution matrix for the empty containers. If the from-and-to notation is reversed, and the numbers in the body of the table are erased (preserving the rim conditions), a return table as shown in Figure 124 will result. Note that the designation on the rim conditions has been changed to "Empties Available" and "Empties Required."

The rim conditions can most easily be interpreted as follows: Department *A,* since it sends out 10 loaded containers per day, will require 10 empty containers per day to keep the system in balance.

Department *B,* since it receives 12 containers of material per day, has 12 empty containers available for distribution per day.

To \ From	B	C	D	E	Empties Required
A					10
B					5
C					8
D					9
E					8
Empties Available	12	11	9	8	40 \ 40

Fig. 124. Return Table

To \ From	B	C	D	E	Empties Required
A	−.62	−.37	−.23	−.35	10
B	0	−.75	−.80	−.65	5
C	−.75	0	−.21	−.15	8
D	−.80	−.21	0	−.45	9
E	−.65	−.15	−.45	0	8
Empties Available	12	11	9	8	40 \ 40

Fig. 125. Distribution Matrix—Empty-Container Distribution

This, then describes a distribution problem. The return table requires merely the addition of the time values for moving an empty container from the various sources to the various destinations. This can be noted as shown in Figure 125, and the familiar distribution matrix emerges.

The numbers in the body of the array represent the time, in decimal hours, required to move an empty container from the source to the destination. For example, it requires 0.62 hour to move an empty container from department *B* to department *A;* 0.37 hour to move an empty container from department *C* to department *A;* etc. These time values are expressed as negative, since it is required to minimize the time spent in returning empties.

One might question why several of the squares, particularly those containing zeros, are left in the array. In this particular problem it takes no time to move an empty: for example, from *B* to *B*. However, in another problem it may actually require some time; i.e., the container may have to be moved from one location to another location, or from one end to the other end of the department, and hence would require time. Including these squares in the array, though it has no effect on the time requirements, will make this a generally applicable approach.

Any of the distribution methods can be employed to solve the problem as shown in Figure 125. In fact, this problem is so simple that inspection should yield the optimum immediately. Figure 126 illustrates the optimum solution to the distribution matrix. The *R* and *K* values have been included so that one can quickly verify the optimality of the solution.

To \ From	B $K_1 = -.62$	C $K_2 = -.37$	D $K_3 = -.23$	E $K_4 = -.35$	Empties Required
A $R_1 = 0$	−.62 (7)	−.37 (3)	−.23 (0)	−.35 (0)	10
B $R_2 = .62$	0 (5)	−.75	−.80	−.65	5
C $R_3 = .37$	−.75	0 (8)	−.21	−.15	8
D $R_4 = .23$	−.80	−.21	0 (9)	−.45	9
E $R_5 = .35$	−.65	−.15	−.45	0 (8)	8
Empties Available	12	11	9	8	40

Fig. 126. Optimum Solution—Empty-Container Distribution

The solution is degenerate, as one might suspect, since several of the individual rim conditions are identical. This, then, provides for the distribution of empty containers in the minimum total time, and completes the third phase in the development of the total problem.

The material movement, from the initial survey, and the optimum empty-container distribution plan can be tabulated for more convenient reference as shown in Figure 127.

Material Deliveries			Optimum Empty Container Returns		
From	To	No. Loads	From	To	No. Loads
A	$\underline{C}$	6	$\underline{B}$	A	7
A	$\underline{D}$	3	$\underline{C}$	A	3
A	$\underline{E}$	1	$\underline{B}$	B	5
B	$\underline{C}$	1	$\underline{C}$	C	8
B	$\underline{E}$	4	$\underline{D}$	D	9
C	$\underline{B}$	3	$\underline{E}$	E	8
C	$\underline{D}$	5			
D	$\underline{B}$	2			
D	$\underline{C}$	4			
D	$\underline{E}$	3			
E	$\underline{B}$	7			
E	$\underline{D}$	1			

Fig. 127. Material and Container Movement Summary

It is required now to develop lift-truck schedules that will accomplish both the material deliveries and the empty container distribution. This can be accomplished if round trips are developed that alternately schedule the delivery of a load and then the delivery of an empty container, beginning and ending at the same location. For example, one round trip could begin at department A and deliver a load of material to department C, returning to A with an empty. In more abbreviated notation this is

$$A\text{–}\underline{C}\text{–}A$$

where the department receiving a delivery of material is underlined.

The round trip (a two-leg round trip) can be accomplished three times since only three empty containers must be returned to A from C. This round trip would then leave three A to $\underline{C}$ trips to be accomplished and will completely cancel out the three $\underline{C}$ to A trips.

More round trips can be assembled in a similar manner, each one canceling some of the trips to be accomplished.

If the round trips are developed with alternate loaded and empty moves, then all the required material and container deliveries can be accomplished.

Wide choice in round trips is possible, as long as they do not violate the material and container movements of Figure 127. This point will be amplified very shortly.

One possible set of round trips is as shown in Figure 128.

		No. Loads
2 Leg Trips		
(1)	A–C–A (Trip loaded A to C—unloaded C to A)	3
4 Leg Trips		
(2)	A–D–D–B–A	2
(3)	A–C–C–B–A	3
(4)	A–E–E–B–A	1
(5)	B–E–E–B–B	4
(6)	C–D–D–C–C	4
(7)	D–E–E–D–D	1
6 Leg Trips		
(8)	A–D–D–E–E–B–A	1
8 Leg Trips		
(9)	B–C–C–D–D–E–E–B–B	1

Fig. 128. A Possible Set of Round Trips to Accomplish the Required Material and Container Distributions

The round trips (Fig. 128) have been organized into 2-, 4-, 6-, and 8-leg trips and have been numbered for further reference in subsequent discussion.

The round trips can be thought of as describing more or less circular paths interconnecting several of the five departments.

It is interesting to note the implications inherent in trip 9. Many organizations, in attempting to control the material handling activity, assign a lift truck and driver to particular areas within the plant. Trip 9 is one of the trips in an optimum handling program that contacts all but one department in the plant. This, then, points out the fallacy in the scheme that limits material handling equipment to a particular area in a plant.

The appropriate time values can be assigned to each of the round trips, based on the time data provided by the labor standards department. The average time required to accomplish the round trip A–$\underline{C}$–A must include the elements:

Pick up material container at A	(Load)
Deliver material to C	(Travel loaded)
Unload at C	(Unload)
Pick up an empty container at C	(Load)
Deliver empty container to A	(Travel with empty)
Unload empty container at A	(Unload)

Adding these various elemental times will provide the average time required to accomplish the A–$\underline{C}$–A round trip. In this case, the time required is 1.17 hours. (The complete tabulation of time data need not be reproduced here.) Similar tabulations will determine the average time requirements for every round trip. These average time requirements are as shown in Figure 129.

Round Trip No.	No. of Trips	Time per Trip, hours	Total Time hours
①	3	1.17	3.51
②	2	2.45	4.90
③	3	2.73	8.19
④	1	2.55	2.55
⑤	4	2.32	9.28
⑥	4	1.28	5.12
⑦	1	1.84	1.84
⑧	1	3.36	3.36
⑨	1	3.98	3.98
		Total Time	42.73 hours

Fig. 129. Average Time Requirements for the Various Round Trips

It is obvious that none of these trips in themselves are suitable as an 8-hour assignment for a lift truck and driver. However, the round trips, since they all represent more or less circular interconnected trips, can be rather easily partitioned or combined to provide assignments of suitable size.

Here one might be prone to develop assignments at or very near 8 hours' duration. However, here several points must be emphasized. Assignments at or very near 8 hours' duration would be unsatisfactory, since all the time values used are average time values. This means that an 8-hour assignment could be accomplished approximately 50 per cent of the time in 8 hours. The range or variability of the total time will depend upon the variability of each of the elemental times. The total time for an 8-hour assignment might vary as much as an hour or two, depending on the plant situation, and the possible unexpected delays that may be encountered. Then too an 8-hour assignment would leave no time available for accomplishing the less-than-once-per-day and the unplanned material movements that might be required in a particular day's operation.

An assignment then, somewhat nearer 5 to 6 hours of the 8-hour day would leave a degree of flexibility, to permit time for most of the possible delays, and to leave time available for accomplishing the unplanned material movements that are bound to occur. An assignment of 5 to 6 hours will reduce the handling equipment requirements in all probability, since a 65 to 75 per cent assignment represents a better than 50 per cent improvement over an average utilization of 40 per cent.

The round trips, since they are interconnected at the various departments, can be rather easily made up into suitable assignments. For example, round trip 9 and two trips of round trip 1 would result in a 6.32-hour assignment for a scheduled utilization of 79 per cent. In a somewhat similar manner, one can develop more round-trip assignments requiring between 5 and 6 hours. Here it can be seen that a considerable degree of flexibility is possible, not only in developing the round-trip assignments, but in establishing the initial round trips also (Fig. 128). The important point is that all required moves, loaded and empty, are accomplished. With practice, the development of truck assignments becomes a relatively easy task.

One possible arrangement of trip assignments for eight trucks is as shown in Figure 130.

Note that the assignments vary from 4.64 hours to 6.32 hours. With more time and effort it may be possible to reduce this variance if desired. However, the variation is usually not critical and presents no major obstacle in the problem.

No. of Trucks	Round Trips	Average Time hours	Scheduled Utilization, Per Cent
1	⑨ + ⅔ ①	6.32	79
1	⑥ + ⅓ ①	6.29	78.6
1	⑦ + ⑧	5.20	65
1	⅔ ③	5.46	68.3
1	⅓ ③ + ④	5.28	66
2	⑤	4.64	58
1	②	4.90	61.3

Average planned utilization 65.5% for eight trucks

Fig. 130. Trip Assignments for Eight Trucks

In a real plant situation, the major advantage of this approach to the material handling problem will become obvious at this point. In all probability, the truck assignments will involve fewer trucks than were formerly required, thereby realizing immediate savings in equipment and manpower.

The assignments (Fig. 130) allow time within an 8-hour day for accomplishing the unplanned and less-than-once-per-day material moves. Actually these moves will comprise a minor portion of the total material movements in a well-ordered manufacturing system.

The assignments, of course, would not be presented to the truck drivers in this form. A listing of each leg of the trip in the correct order will usually be sufficient. The assignment can be more detailed to include part number or other suitable identification for each of the successive material movements if this is required or desirable. Usually this assists the driver in identifying his loads of material through the course of the day.

If little variation in trip times and few unplanned material movements are encountered, then, of course, truck assignments can be prepared requiring more time than those shown previously. For example, Figure 131 illustrates the same material movements as assignments for six trucks.

Assignments as shown in Figure 131 should be made only after some experience or with more information than that given for the problem at hand.

Using the Solution. The problem and its solution were based on the average conditions. However, the actual material movements required will probably vary from day to day. Hence it would appear that the entire problem must be set up and solved every day.

No. of Trucks	Round Trips	Average Time hours	Scheduled Utilization, Per Cent
1	2 + ⅓ ③	7.63	95.4
1	7 + ⅔ ③	7.30	91.2
1	⑧ + ⑨	7.34	91.7
2	½ ⑤ + ½ ⑥	7.20	90
1	① + ④	6.06	75.8

Average planned utilization 89% for six trucks

Fig. 131. Trip Assignments for Six Trucks

This is not true. Since the problem was developed and based on average conditions, a degree of variation can be rather easily accommodated on a day-to-day basis.

Day-to-day variations will change the rim conditions of the route table (Fig. 123) and the empty-container return table or distribution matrix (Fig. 126). However, when the rim conditions of the distribution matrix change (assuming a small change in any or all of the numbers), the size of the assignments (stones) will change, but their placement in the matrix will remain unchanged. This means that one relatively untrained in mathematical programming can easily obtain the optimum solution with changed rim conditions. On a day-to-day basis then, the variations will be reflected in adding and/or deleting moves from the summary list (Fig. 127). This requires some modification in the round trips and in the ultimate truck assignment, but these changes, for the most part, are small compared to the total problem.

In a relatively large manufacturing installation, the truck dispatcher successfully accomplishes the day-to-day scheduling for approximately 20 trucks in a situation similar to the sample problem discussed above.

Certainly there will be times when materials are not ready for the truck. The problem is then: what to do? This problem can be rather easily solved where the trucks are radio-dispatched. However, it can also be solved using the usual in-plant telephone system. When a driver reports that material is not ready for him as required in his assignment, the dispatcher can rather easily review the status of the entire material handling activity and provide the driver with one of three possible alternatives. These are:

1. Wait until the material is ready.
2. Pick up someone else's assignment for the remainder of the day.

3. Accomplish one or more unscheduled material moves, and return to the assigned schedule.

The first alternative can be permitted, since a delay safety factor has been included, when preparing a 5- to 6-hour truck assignment. This may be the best or only alternative in some instances. The second alternative is essentially trading assignments between two or more trucks. This is possible, since all the assignments and round trips are interconnected circles. The driver who reported the delay picks up another driver's assignment from that point on. The second driver then follows the first driver's initial assignment from that point on. The third alternative is obvious, since this is a logical time and place to accomplish some of the unplanned material moves.

In the example problem, no mention or consideration was made of the time requirements for the material deliveries. It was assumed, or at least implied, that deliveries any time during the course of the day were satisfactory. This is rarely if, indeed, ever the case in a real manufacturing situation, unless all material movements are accomplished between shifts or on a third shift. In an actual situation, deliveries will have required times at which they must be made. However, relatively few deliveries must be exactly on time, and most of them can be made as much as an hour in advance. In a plant recently investigated, it was found that only 9 deliveries of approximately 65 during the course of the day had to be made at or very near a specific time. In several of these deliveries, the tolerance on time was 10 or 15 minutes at the very most. However, most of the remaining deliveries could be accomplished as much as 3 hours ahead of the required time. This, of course, will vary with the material, quantity per delivery, rate of consumption, and available space for temporary storage.

In preparing the truck schedules, the time requirements can be noted and schedules prepared to accomplish the material movements as required during the day. This does make the preparation of truck schedules somewhat more difficult but not insurmountable.

Another advantage is to be gained with truck scheduling as outlined here, in that a measure of efficiency is available. This can permit objective evaluation of the drivers and can point out those not carrying their part of the work load. Without a definite assignment, an evaluation of the drivers becomes purely subjective. Truck scheduling can be the initial step in providing a measure of a fair day's work, and a higher degree of control, within the indirect labor area of material handling.

In the sample problem, the same container was assumed for the entire operation. This need not be. Several types of containers can be considered without too much difficulty. Those containers having but one origin and destination can be immediately assigned in the movement summary list. Containers having several, but not all possible, origins and destinations, can be so designated in the return-table distribution matrix as a separate row with $-M$ costs wherever distribution is not allowed. This then permits a wide variety of containers to be considered in the same problem. However, the problem becomes more difficult as the number of containers increases, and the potential savings via mathematical programming are reduced.

In another problem recently investigated, it was found that the bulk of handling was in fiberboard cartons, which were broken down and disposed of by the sweeper. The problem was no different from that illustrated here, except that the return table represented, for the most part, the redistribution of empty trucks instead of empty containers. The mathematical programming then minimized the empty-container redistribution time and the dead-heading time. This problem involved true dead heading or moving absolutely empty between locations.

The time values in the sample problem implied a relatively large manufacturing plant. However, this analysis is equally valid in a smaller installation. The potential gain may be more limited in a smaller plant. One problem encountered involved move times from 3 to 15 minutes each. This presented no apparent obstacle to solving the problem.

SUMMARY

Mathematical programming was illustrated here as a tool for improving on nonautomated material handling. The problem, though simple, served to illustrate the phases required in its analysis and solution. This application is of particular interest also, in that it shows mathematical programming in its truer proportions: namely, as a means of solving a very small part of the total problem. Many are prone to think that mathematical programming represents the major portion of the problem, whereas in many instances it is a relative small part of the total problem.

The approach illustrated in the sample problem is being used on a daily basis in a large government installation. The trucks are radio-dispatched, and the same dispatcher prepares the truck assignments and controls the material handling operation. The application of mathematical programming resulted in an improvement in the operation, with a reduction in required manpower and equipment. This general type of analysis can be employed to obtain a measure of comparison between two or more plant layouts. The layout requiring the least amount of material handling time or distance will be best from the material handling standpoint. In this respect, the applications of mathematical programming and of "travel charting"[53] are somewhat similar. The travel-chart approach is somewhat less quantitative.

The analysis presented here can be very helpful in providing a valid basis for a cost comparison between a nonautomated and an automated handling system. In many cases, a new material handling system is justified by comparison with the existing material handling. It stands to reason, then, that this comparison is at least partially invalid when the existing material handling system is operating in such an inefficient state. This particular application of mathematical programming is of interest then because it implies improving upon the existing system prior to making a change.

---

[53] W. P. Smith, "Travel Charting," *AIIE Journal,* V. 6, No. 1, January 1955, pp. 13–15.

10.

Job and Salary Evaluation[54]

Mathematical programming applied to job and salary evaluation offers a new and useful approach to solving one of management's most elusive problems. The discussion here will be limited to salaried and supervisory-type jobs although it can be extended equally well to other job classifications.

The mathematical programming part of the problem is, as in several of the previous applications, a relatively small part of the total job-evaluation problem. Job evaluation must be based upon a complete job description, which in itself must stem from an adequate definition of the objectives of the organization. Job evaluation can be successfully accomplished only after the following points have been crystallized:

1. Objectives of the organization.

[54] I do not profess to be an expert in this rather specialized area and certainly do not necessarily advocate this approach as the only solution to the job-evaluation problem. This example, however, is presented primarily for its academic interest, since it points to a general class of problems solvable by mathematical programming. Mathematical programming has been successfully applied to job and salary evaluation in one large manufacturing concern, and so this is not a purely academic application.

2. Functions necessary to attain the objectives.

3. Jobs necessary to accomplish the functions.

4. Job definition and description (including the defining of authority and responsibility).

When this preliminary work has been accomplished, then a job-evaluation scheme can be developed. The essential characteristic of any job-evaluation program is consistency; it need not be absolutely correct, but the evaluations must be consistently administered to be of any real value.

Often job evaluation is accomplished by correlation analysis. Basically this type of analysis determines which factor or characteristic contributes most to success in a particular job. It is somewhat limited, in that relatively few factors can be included in the analysis. Then, too, it is of limited value when success can be attributed to many factors instead of a few. Job evaluation based on mathematical programming is different, in that there is virtually no limit to the number of factors that can be considered in the analysis. Essentially this approach calculates relative weights for each factor, such that the ranking of positions corresponds to the hierarchy of the organization. This analysis then provides a measure of the relative importance of each factor for the jobs within an organization.

The job-evaluation problem can be analyzed and solved in six phases. These are:

1. Determination of the factors to be included in the analysis. This can usually be accomplished by an initial survey of the individuals in the organization, followed by several meetings to crystallize all the factors. To be certain, there will probably be some compromises, but this is not necessarily a major problem. This phase of the study is extremely difficult where job descriptions are poorly written or altogether lacking. This phase of the study can provide useful information for improving ambiguous and poorly written descriptions.

2. Development of a well-defined rating system for each factor. Here a major portion of the consistency in the job evaluation is obtained. A rating for each factor is established, and each rating for each factor is carefully defined. This avoids the difficulties inherent in using the usually loosely defined and nebulous terms such as average, above average, and below average. For example, consider the following rating system for the factor education:

Rating	Definition
0	High school graduate
1	Some college—no degree
2	Bachelor's degree
3	Master's degree
4	Ph.D. degree

This is an objective factor. Consider the following rating for the somewhat subjective factor, supervisory ability:

Rating	Definition
0	None required
1	Ability to supervise a small group of non-technical people on relatively continuous job assignments
2	Ability to supervise a small group of technical and/or professional-type people
3	Ability to supervise a large group of people with several subordinate supervisors
4	Ability to supervise and coordinate the activities of several large groups via a team of subordinate line supervisors

Similar ratings can be prepared for every factor in the analysis. The number of ratings can vary; however, practical limitations are soon reached. Too few ratings will not sufficiently delineate between differences in abilities, and too many will require definitions with shades of meaning resulting in a loss of clarity. A rating system 0 through 4 seems generally suitable for job evaluation.

3. Determination of the rating of each factor for each job. This can be accomplished, based upon the job description as well as the responsibility level of the job. This rating becomes the basis for the mathematical formulation.

4. Determination of the relative weights of each factor. This is accomplished by mathematical programming. The mathematical formulation establishes a point system for a number of key jobs (those jobs where a difference in level is unquestionable) based upon the hierarchy of the organization. The total points for a position are based upon the hierarchy curve (or salary curve in some cases) of the organization. Hence, the relative weights are calculated so that they are consistent with the job rating and the hierarchy.

5. Calculation of point ratings for remaining jobs. The calculated relative weights are used to evaluate and position the remaining jobs in the hierarchy. If the results obtained are in error, i.e., several jobs are definitely out of place, then, either the mathematical formulation must be reworked with more key positions, or a significant factor (or factors) has been overlooked in the analysis.

6. Evaluation of the employee, his job, and his salary. This is the real end result. Here a much more objective appraisal of the employee, his salary and his job is possible.

The mathematical analysis can best be seen in a small illustrative example. Assume that an organization has already accomplished the first three phases of the study.[55] The problem is ready then for the mathematical analysis. At this point, it is necessary to determine the set-up of the hierarchy within the organization. This can and will vary between organizations; however, it must be known before the mathematics can be applied. Figure 132 illustrates some forms of hierarchy organizations. Line *C* is generally representative of most organizations.

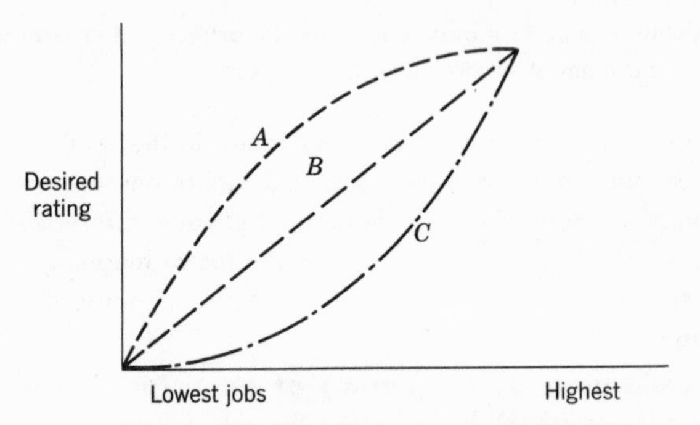

Fig. 132. Organization Hierarchy

The hierarchy can be developed according to salary range, but this is not a requirement. In cases where salary and bonus are employed, such as sales positions, the salary alone is not a particularly good indicator. The rating can be successfully developed with only a very broad indication of salary ranges, and thereby will approximate the general pay scale without fixing the solution exactly as to salary.

Four key jobs have been selected and their rating is as shown in Figure 133.

---

[55] It must not be construed that these phases are unimportant for, if these cannot be accomplished, the entire study is stymied. The example shown here is primarily to illustrate the mathematics employed.

Job	Education	Experience	Judgment	Supervisory Ability
		Factors		
Manager	3	4	4	4
Superintendent	3	4	4	3
General Foreman	2	3	3	3
Foreman	2	1	3	1
Assistant foreman	1	0	1	0

Fig. 133. Key Jobs and Their Ratings[56]

The organization hierarchy indicates that a rating system should establish points for the jobs as follows:

Job	Points
Manager	20,000
General foreman	10,000
Assistant foreman	2,000

The mathematical formulation can then be prepared. Let

x_1 = the relative weight of the factor education
x_2 = the relative weight of the factor experience
x_3 = the relative weight of the factor judgment
x_4 = the relative weight of the factor supervisory ability

then part of the formulation representing those key jobs with desired point ratings is as follows:

Manager $$3x_1 + 4x_2 + 4x_3 + 4x_4 \leq 20{,}000 \quad (1)$$

General foreman $$2x_1 + 3x_2 + 3x_3 + 3x_4 \cong 10{,}000 \quad (2)$$

Assistant foreman $$x_1 + x_3 \geq 2{,}000 \quad (3)$$

Note here that three types of mathematical relationships are represented. The restriction (1) and requirement (3) keep the point values within the required range. The approximation (2) is mathematically better than an equation since the general foreman job rating need not be exactly equal to 10,000 points.

Several additional relationships must be included in the formulation. Obviously the calculated ratings for the key positions cannot violate the ranking requirements; i.e., the superintendent job cannot have a rating superior to the manager job. Even if actual

[56] In a real situation, more key positions would probably be included and certainly many more factors. The problem is purposely abbreviated here for clarity.

numerical values were listed for all positions, this would be necessary. The formulas to express the ranking are relatively simple. Since the superintendent rating must be less than the manager rating, then the difference between them must be at least zero, or:

$$0 \cdot x_1 + 0 \cdot x_2 + 0 \cdot x_3 + x_4 \geq 0$$

This will assure that the superintendent job rating can never exceed the manager job rating. Here it might be desirable to specify some minimum point spread: say 500 points. Mathematically this would be

$$0 \cdot x_1 + 0 \cdot x_2 + 0 \cdot x_3 + x_4 \geq 500$$

This would assure a minimum of 500 points difference between the two positions. This must be accomplished in a similar manner for every other position. Assuming at least a 500-point difference between ratings, the formulation must then include:

$$x_4 \geq 500 \qquad (4)$$

$$x_1 + x_2 + x_3 \geq 500 \qquad (5)$$

$$2x_2 + 2x_4 \geq 500 \qquad (6)$$

$$x_1 + x_2 + 2x_3 + x_4 \geq 500 \qquad (7)$$

These four expressions assure a minimum of 500 points spread between job ratings. All seven relationships adequately express the problem. The objective in this case is to minimize the slack or deviation in the expressions (1), (2), and (3). The entire problem ready for the initial simplex matrix is then as follows:

The system:

$$3x_1 + 4x_2 + 4x_3 + 4x_4 + W_1 = 20{,}000 \qquad (1)$$

$$2x_1 + 3x_2 + 3x_3 + 3x_4 - W_2 + W_3 = 10{,}000 \qquad (2)$$

$$x_1 + x_3 - W_4 + U_1 = 2{,}000 \qquad (3)$$

$$x_4 - W_5 + U_2 = 500 \qquad (4)$$

$$x_1 + x_2 + x_3 - W_6 + U_3 = 500 \qquad (5)$$

$$2x_2 + 2x_4 - W_7 + U_4 = 500 \qquad (6)$$

$$x_1 + x_2 + 2x_3 + x_4 - W_8 + U_5 = 500 \qquad (7)$$

The objective:

$$0 \cdot x_1 + 0 \cdot x_2 + \cdots - W_1 - W_2 - W_3 + 0 \cdot W_4 + 0 \cdot W_5 \cdots - MU_1 - MU_2 \cdots = \text{maximum}$$

The problem is represented then in a 7×17 simplex array. The solution to this mathematical model will provide relative weights for each of the factors, consistent within the specifications of the model.[57]

The calculated results for the weights of the various factors (x's) can be applied to the remaining jobs to obtain their respective rating. The same calculated results can be applied to evaluating the men in the jobs. This can provide a much more objective evaluation and one that can result in constructive criticism of any shortcomings.

One might question here that the analysis and evaluation considers factors or characteristics required by the job and possessed by the individual in the job. To be certain, an individual's past performance will enter into the evaluation through those factors required for successful past performance. It is conceivable too that this type of analysis, in that it includes many factors, can detect the competent technician or lower-level supervisor, who would fail or do a marginal job with a promotion beyond his capabilities. The job-evaluation scheme presented here can be very useful in obtaining a rapid, objective evaluation of a potential employee. Several interviews can provide a reasonably valid evaluation of the individual's talents which can be rather easily compared with the requirements of the job.

A job-evaluation scheme as outlined above can be very useful in the promotion problem. Here it is possible to see the problem as one of distribution: one in which men are distributed to jobs so that the difference between the man's point value and his job's point value is as small as possible. This may not necessarily result

[57] It is of interest here to note that the objective accomplishes a series of short straight lines or broken lines conforming with the hierarchy curve. These straight lines representing the approximation to the hierarchy curve are such that the sum of the absolute differences is a minimum. This then matches a series of short straight lines to a curve by a sum of absolute differences method.

in the actual best solution, but it can serve as a guide for the final management action.[58]

SUMMARY

Job and salary evaluation presents a somewhat different application of mathematical programming. In this type of problem, mathematical programming can provide a more detailed analysis than that obtainable by correlation analysis. Possible advantages are:

1. Consistent employee evaluation and rating throughout the organization.

2. A more valid indication of an individual's worth.

3. A more valid justification for salary increases.

4. Better employee counciling. This can be more objective and actually assist the employee in his self-development.

5. Aid in solving promotion problems.

Certainly, many of these advantages can be gained with a variety of evaluation schemes. However, this application does illustrate the thorough and far-reaching analysis dictated by the general operations research approach to the problem.

This example is interesting since it points to more possible applications. Some of these are:

1. Academic testing—it seems feasible that an analysis of, say, college freshman tests can provide a better prediction of academic potential.

2. Market research—it is possible to apply this type of analysis to determining the best of several possible sites for retail outlets, factories, or warehouses. The analysis is based upon the factors influencing costs and/or profits in present operations. This is used to obtain a more objective appraisal of several possible sites for a new operation.

3. Analysis of advertising expenditures—here again the relative weights (or profitability) of the factors affecting advertising can be devel-

[58] This is in the category of the assignment problem. Several methods have been developed for this type of problem, notably by Kuhn and Dwyer. The regular distribution methods are satisfactory for small problems. However, these problems are so degenerate that they can cause considerable trouble in solution via the distribution methods.

oped and used to evaluate the potential return of advertising dollars in the several advertising media. This analysis must be somewhat more cautious, since one cannot absolutely attribute an increase in sales to an increase in advertising

4. Tool analysis—the relative weights of the factors affecting tool life can be determined, so that one can predict more accurately the expected tool life, and hence cost, for a manufacturing problem.

5. Classroom allocation—in a school, this analysis can be employed to determine the room assignments for classes based upon the physical factors of the rooms and the requirements of the classes.

These possible applications are offered primarily as thought starters. It is interesting to note that usually the greatest limitation to mathematical programming is the ingenuity of the individual applying it. Actually this volume could not possibly contain all the possible applications of mathematical programming.

11.
Summary

Several methods and applications of mathematical programming have been presented in relatively nonmathematical terms. These methods offer a means of solving a wide variety of problems which have been approached intuitively or not at all in the past. Mathematical programming, though it is not a panacea for all problem situations, offers a new approach that can provide management with more and better information on which to base decisions.

The applications that have been presented here are by no means even representative of the wide variety of problems solvable by mathematical programming. Though the applications can be classified as distribution or allocation problems, the variety of applications is almost limitless. Some published applications other than those presented here are as follows:

Agricultural economics[59]
Blending aviation gasolines
Evaluating military contract bids
Personnel assignment
Shipping with least-ballast requirements

[59] Many applications have been published primarily in the *Journal of Farm Economics*. Many applications have been in the area of farm management: i.e., stock-feeding and crop-planting programs.

Optimal test design[60]
Assembly-line balancing[61]
Structural-design evaluation
Optical filter design

These and more applications have been presented in the literature to date. There is every indication that this list will continue to expand as time passes. One of the limitations to expanded applications of mathematical programming is the ingenuity of the analysts and their ability to recognize a possible application. Here is where practice can develop proficiency. Actually a need exists for people adequately trained, who can recognize and formulate the problem and, finally, assess the solution and its various alternatives as meaningful courses of action for the problem. These people must be proficient in the required mathematics and yet capable of conversing with management in terms they (management) readily understand.

The problem of semantics is present even among well-trained professional people. For example, an economist, a mathematician, and an industrial engineer, all trained in mathematical programming, would have at least some differences in interpretation of a solution, based on their individual perspective of a problem.

The mathematical programming approach to solving industrial problems is much superior to many of the intuitive methods employed today. It is interesting, however, to discover that often the intuitive solution by an experienced person, particularly in a machine-assignment problem, will be very close to the optimum solution obtained by mathematical programming. This, however, does not discount the value of the mathematical formulation and solution, since any individual with only nominal experience can always obtain the very best answer with mathematical programming. By contrast, years of experience are usually required to develop any valid intuitive method of solution.

Mathematical programming was limited initially to static analysis. As developments progressed, the production planning problem

---

[60] This and the preceding applications are presented in the publication of the *Symposium on Linear Inequalities and Programming,* Project SCOOP, A. Orden and L. Goldstein, eds., Planning Research Division Director of Management Analysis Service, Comptroller, Headquarters U. S. Air Force, Washington, April 1, 1952.

[61] This and the following two applications are presented in the publication of *Second Symposium on Linear Programming,* two volumes. Washington, D. C., January 27–29, 1955.

was presented as the first example of dynamic analysis (incorporating more than one period of time) with mathematical programming. The planning problem presented in this text is an example of such a dynamic analysis. However, mathematical programming is, in the main, limited to a more static type of analysis.

Usually the most difficult task in mathematical programming is obtaining the necessary factual information. Often the digging for the required information will uncover previously hidden problems, which when exposed can be easily solved. It is not inconceivable that the gains derived in solving these previously hidden problems may far outweigh the gains from mathematical programming. In fact, the problem to be solved may be reduced to where the solution is obvious, thereby making mathematical programming unnecessary for the solution. This, however, does not discount the value of mathematical programming, since it involves more of a philosophy of problem approach than merely the solution methods presented here. In the final analysis, anything that forces a critical look at what is being done can be of value to an organization.

Another difficulty often encountered is attempting to pinpoint the objective. This is often difficult even for management to specify. The objective may be maximum equipment utilization, minimum cost, maximum profit, maximum number of pieces, etc. Each of these objectives may yield a different solution to the same model. The problem used to illustrate the simplex method is just such a model, where different solutions may be obtained for maximum profit, maximum equipment utilization, and maximum number of pieces produced. If management cannot clearly envision and state the objective, then mathematical programming is stopped before it has even begun. The alternative in such a case is to solve the problem with the several possible objective functions.

In many problems, an economist is interested not only in the optimum solution, but also in the effect upon this solution of a small change in the objective function. For example, a manufacturer is interested not only in an optimum allocation of resources for his manufacturing enterprise, but also in the effect upon the manufacturing system caused by a slight change in labor or material costs. This type of problem has been approached with the parametric objective function:[62] a means whereby one can solve a

[62] T. Saaty and S. Gass, "Parametric Objective Function," Part I, *Journal of Operations Research Society of America,* V. 2, No. 3. August 1954, pp. 316–319; Part 2, V. 3, No. 4, November 1955, pp. 395–401. See also A. S. Manne, "Notes on Parametric Linear Programming," Rand Report, December 1953.

problem with a variety of parameters affecting the objective function. While this requires more work, it does supply management with more and better information for decisions.

Mathematical programming, while it is a relatively small part of the total field of operations research, exhibits the operations research philosophy. Mathematical programming forces the new look of operations research, namely, the more complete mathematical analysis of a problem, into areas that heretofore relied entirely upon judgment, experience, and intuition. To be sure, mathematical programming cannot and will not replace judgment and experience, but it can be of immeasurable assistance to the people who have to make decisions.

Bibliography

RELATIVELY EASY READING

Beckwith, R. E., and R. Vaswani. "The Assignment Problem—A Special Case of Linear Programming." *AIIE Journal,* Vol. 8, No. 3, May–June 1957, pp. 167–172.

Bishop, G. T. "On a Problem of Production Scheduling." *Journal of the Operations Research Society of America,* Vol. 5, No. 1, February 1957, pp. 97–103.

Bowman, Edward H. "Production Scheduling by the Transportation Method of Linear Programming." *Journal of the Operations Research Society of America,* Vol. 4, No. 1, 1956, pp. 100–103.

Brisley, M. D. J. "Assessing Engineering Problems by Operational Research Methods." *Engineer,* Vol. 199, 1955, pp. 803–805.

Churchman, C. W., R. L. Ackoff, and E. L. Arnoff. *Introduction to Operations Research.* New York: John Wiley & Sons, 1957.

Cooper, W. W., and A. Charnes. "The Stepping Stone Method of Explaining Linear Programming Calculations in Transportation Problems." *Management Science,* Vol. 1, No. 1, October 1954.

______"Transportation Scheduling by Linear Programming," *Proceedings of the Conference on Operations Research in Marketing at Case Institute of Technology,* January 1953.

Ferguson, Robert O. "Linear Programming." *American Machinist,* Special Report 389, 1955.

Goland, M., and E. Koenigsberg. "Operations Research Scientific Approach to Management." *Chemical Weekly,* May 21, 1955.

Harrison, Joseph O. Jr. "Linear Programming and Operations Research," *Operations Research for Management.* Baltimore: John Hopkins Press, 1954.

Harvard University Graduate School of Business Administration. *Operations Research Challenge to Modern Management,* August 1954.

Henderson, A., and R. Schlaifer. "Mathematical Programming: Better Information for Better Decision Making." *Harvard Business Review,* May–June 1954.

Herrmann, C. C., and J. F. Magee. "Operations Research for Management." *Harvard Business Review,* July–August 1953, pp. 100–112.

Klein, M., and S. Milberg. "The Application of Linear Programming to Materials Handling." *Modern Material Handling,* February 1955, pp. 80–84.

Kruse, B. "Using Computers to Match Production and Seasonal Trends." *American Business,* Vol. 25, No. 12–13, October 1955.

Lanchester, F. W. *Aircraft in Warfare: The Dawn of the Fourth Arm.* London: Constable & Co., 1916.

Magee, J. F. "Application of Operations Research to Marketing and Related Management Problems." *Journal of Marketing,* Vol. 18, April 1954, pp. 361–369. Discussion by R. L. Ackoff, Vol. 20, July 1955, pp. 47–48.

McCloskey, J. F., et al. *Operations Research for Management.* Baltimore: John Hopkins Press, 1954. (Vol. II, 1956.)

Metzger, R. W. "Linear Programming Can Cut Dead-heading," *Flow Magazine,* May 1957, pp. 78–81+.

Reinfeld, N. W. "VAM: Short-cut to Mathematical Programming." *Tooling and Production,* Vol. 23, No. 1, April 1957, pp. 94–99.

Schultz, A. "Operations Research Related to Production Engineering." American Society of Mechanical Engineers, Paper No. 54-A-221, December 1954.

Scott, Lloyd N. *Naval Consulting Board of the United States.* Washington: Government Printing Office, 1920.

Smith, W. P. "Travel Charting." *AIIE Journal,* Vol. 4, No. 1, January–February 1955, p. 13.

Whitmore, William F. "Edison and Operations Research," *Journal of the Operations Research Society of America,* Vol. 1, No. 2, February 1953, pp. 83–85.

REFERENCES FOR THE MORE MATHEMATICALLY INCLINED

Arnoff, E. L. "The Application of Linear Programming to Production Engineering and Scheduling." American Society of Mechanical Engineers Paper No. 54-A-223, December 1954. 7 pp.

Barankin, E. W. "The Scheduling Problem as an Algebraic Generalization of Ordinary Linear Programming." Industrial Logistics Research Project, University of California, Los Angeles, Discussion Paper No. 19. 16 pp.

Chatto, K. A. "An Application of Operations Research Methods to the Selection of a Processing Plan in a Meat Packing Plant." Unpublished MSIE Thesis, Purdue University, June 1955.

Churchman, C. W., R. L. Ackoff, and E. L. Arnoff. *Introduction to Operations Research.* New York: John Wiley & Sons, 1957.

Dwyer, P. S. *Linear Computations.* New York: John Wiley & Sons, 1951.

Galler, B. A. "704 Program for the Approximate Solution of the Multidimensional Transportation Problem." General Motors Research Staff Report No. 34-782, November 1956. Also Report No. 34-844, March 27, 1957. (Privately circulated.)

Hitchcock, Frank L. "The Distribution of a Product from Several Sources to Numerous Localities." *Journal of Mathematics and Physics,* Vol. 20, 1941, pp. 224–230.

Hoffman, A. J. "Linear Programming." *Applied Mechanics Review,* Vol. 9, No. 5, May 1956, pp. 185–187.

Houthakker, H. C. "On the Numerical Solution of the Transportation Problem." *Journal of the Operations Research Society of America,* Vol. 3, No. 2, May 1955, pp. 210–214.

Manne, Alan S. *Scheduling of Petroleum Refinery Operations.* Cambridge, Massachusetts: Harvard University Press, 1956. 181 pp.

Metzger, R. W. "Development of Refined Mathematical Programming Methods for Industrial Engineering Problems." Unpublished MS Thesis, Michigan State University, 1957.

Morse, P. M., and G. E. Kimball. *Methods of Operations Research.* Massachusetts Institute of Technology and John Wiley & Sons, 1951.

Project SCOOP. A. Orden and L. Goldstein (editors). *Symposium on Linear Inequalities and Programming.* Washington: Headquarters U. S. Air Force and National Bureau of Standards, 1952.

Saaty, T. L. "Approximation to the Value of the Objective Function in Linear Programming by the Method of Partitions." *Journal of the Operations Research Society of America,* Vol. 4: No. 3, June 1956, p. 352.

——— and S. Gass. "Parametric Objective Function," Part I. *Journal of the Operations Society of America,* Vol. 2, No. 3, August 1954, pp. 316–319. Part II. Vol. 3, No. 4, November 1955, pp. 395–401.

Salveson, M. E. "A Mathematical Theory of Production Planning and Scheduling." *Journal of Industrial Engineering,* Vol. 4, No. 1, February 1953, pp. 3–6.

Salveson, M. E., and R. C. Canning. "Electronic Production Control." Industrial Logistics Research Project, University of California, Los Angeles, Research Report No. 17.

——— "On a Quantitative Method in Production Planning and Scheduling." *Econometrica,* Vol. 20, No. 4, October 1952, pp. 554–590.

Second Symposium on Linear Programming. Two Volumes. Washington, U. S. Air Force and Bureau of Standards, 1955.

——— Foulkes, J. "Linear Programming and Structural Design." pp. 177–184.

——— Gainen, Leon. "Linear Programming in Bid Evaluation." pp. 29–38.

——— Jacobs, Walter. "Military Applications of Linear Programming." pp. 1–28.

——— Salveson, M. E. "Assembly Line Balancing Problem." pp. 55–102.

——— Tintner, G. "Stochastic Linear Programming with Applications to Agricultural Economics." pp. 197–228.

——— Votaw, D. F. "Programming under Conditions of Uncertainty." pp. 187–196.

Slade, J. J. "Some Observations on Formal Models for Programming." American Society of Mechanical Engineers. Paper No. 54-A-241, December 1954.

Symonds, G. H. *Linear Programming: The Solution of Refinery Problems.* New York: Esso Standard Oil Company, 1955. 74 pp.

Vajda, S. *The Theory of Games and Linear Programming.* New York: John Wiley & Sons, 1956.

Wagner, H. M. "A Two-Phase Method for the Simplex Tableau." *Journal of the Operations Research Society of America,* Vol. 4, No. 4, August 1956, pp. 443–447.

TECHNICAL REFERENCES

Charnes, A., W. W. Cooper, and A. Henderson. *An Introduction to Linear Programming.* New York: John Wiley & Sons, 1953.

Dantzig, G. B. "Application of the Simplex Method to a Transportation Problem." T. C. Koopmans (editor). *Activity Analysis of Production and Allocation.* New York: John Wiley & Sons, 1951.

Dorfman, Robert. *Application of Linear Programming to the Theory of the Firm.* Berkeley, California: University of California Press, 1951.

Dwyer, P. S. "Maximum Group Assembly Sums." Report submitted to Air Force Personnel and Research Center, Randolph Field, Texas.

______"The Solution of the Hitchcock Transportation Problem with a Method of Reduced Matrices." University of Michigan, December 1955. (Hectographed.)

Eisemann, Kurt. "Linear Programming." *Quarterly of Applied Mathematics,* Vol. 13, No. 3, October 1955, pp. 209–323.

______"Linear Programming—Recursive Generation of Vectors for the Modified Simplex Method." New York: IBM, 1956. (Mimeographed.)

Koopmans, T. C. *Activity Analysis of Production and Allocation.* New York: John Wiley & Sons, 1951. 404 pp.

Kuhn, H. W. "The Hungarian Method for the Assignment Problem." *Naval Research Logistics Quarterly,* Vol. 2, 1955, pp. 83–97.

Manne, Alan S. "Notes on Parametric Linear Programming." Rand Report, December 1953.

McAllister, G. Eric. "Statistical Decision Theory." Industrial Logistics Research Project, University of California, Los Angeles, Technical Report No. 10, 1953.

Project SCOOP. A. Orden and L. Goldstein (editors). *Symposium on Linear Inequalities and Programming.* Washington: Headquarters U. S. Air Force and National Bureau of Standards, 1952.

Saline, L. E. "Quadratic Programming of Interdependent Activities for Optimum Performance." American Society of Mechanical Engineers. Paper No. 54–A–58, November 1954. 21 pp.

Salveson, M. E., and R. C. Canning. "On an Assembly-Line Balancing Problem." *ASME Transactions,* Vol. 77, No. 6, August 1955, pp. 939–948.

Second Symposium on Linear Programming. Two Volumes. Washington: U. S. Air Force and Bureau of Standards, 1955.

______Foulkes, J. "Linear Programming and Structural Design." pp. 177–184.

______Gainen, Leon. "Linear Programming in Bid Evaluation." pp. 29–38.

______Jacobs, Walter. "Military Applications of Linear Programming." pp. 1–28.

______Salveson, M. E. "Assembly Line Balancing Problem." pp. 55–102.

______Tintner, G. "Stochastic Linear Programming with Applications to Agricultural Economics." pp. 197–228.

______Votaw, D. F. "Programming Under Conditions of Uncertainty." pp. 187–196.

Symonds, G. H. *Linear Programming: The Solution of Refinery Problems.* New York: Esso Standard Oil Company, 1955. 74 pp.

Vajda, S. *The Theory of Games and Linear Programming.* New York: John Wiley & Sons, 1956.

Wald, Abraham. *Statistical Decisions Functions.* New York: John Wiley & Sons, 1950. 179 pp.

Index